The Air Pilot's **Manual**

EASA Supplement

Operational Procedures

Jonathan Shooter

Nothing in this manual supersedes any legislation, rules, regulations or procedures contained in any operational document issued by The Stationery Office, the Civil Aviation Authority, the manufacturers of aircraft, engines and systems, or by the operators of aircraft throughout the world. Note that as maps and charts are changed regularly, those extracts reproduced in this book must not be used for flight planning or flight operations.

Origination by Pooleys Flight Equipment Limited.

Published by Pooleys-Air Pilot Publishing Limited
Highdown House
Shoreham Airport
West Sussex, BN43 5PB, England
Tel: +44(0)208 207 3749
Web: www.pooleys.com
e-mail: sales@pooleys.com

The Air Pilot's **Manual**

EASA Operational Procedures

Contents

Editorial Team

Jonathan Shooter

Jonathan had his first trial lesson on his twelfth birthday before going on to gain his PPL with the help of an RAF flying scholarship. He went on to fly with the University Air Squadron before gaining airline sponsorship in conjunction with one of Europe's largest flying schools. He taught the PPL and associated ratings at Elstree aerodrome before gaining an internal promotion to teach the CPL and Instrument Rating at the commercial college at Cranfield aerodrome. In 2004 he was awarded a flying bursary from The Air League. After two years he joined his sponsoring airline and flew the Dash 8 Q400 throughout Europe. In 2005 he joined Europe's largest tour operator and flew the Boeing 757, 767, A320 & A321 both on short and long haul operations. He currently flies the 737NG and has over 7000 hrs with 1500 hrs instructional experience on commercial courses. He holds European, Canadian and American airline transport licences and is an authorised PPL examiner for both single and multi-engine aeroplanes.

Dorothy Saul-Pooley LLB(Hons) FRAeS

Dorothy holds an ATPL (A) and a CPL (H), and is both an instructor and examiner on aeroplanes and an instructor on helicopters. She is Head of Training for a school dedicated to running Flight Instructor courses at Shoreham. She is also a CAA Flight Instructor Examiner. In addition, having qualified as a solicitor in 1982, Dorothy acted for many years as a consultant specialising in aviation and insurance liability issues, and has lectured widely on air law and insurance issues. This highly unusual combination of qualifications led to her appointment as Honorary Solicitor to the Guild of Air Pilots and Navigators (GAPAN). Dorothy is a Fellow of the Royal Aeronautical Society, past Chairman of both the GAPAN Instructor Committee and the Education & Training Committee, as well as serving as a Warden on their Court. She is currently Master Elect and will be installed as Master in March 2014. In 2003 she was awarded the Jean Lennox Bird Trophy for her contribution to aviation and support of Women in Aviation and the BWPA (British Women Pilots Association). In 2013 Dorothy was awarded the prestigious Master Air Pilot Certificate by GAPAN. A regular contributor to seminars and conferences, Dorothy is the author and editor of a number of flying training books and has published articles in legal and insurance journals.

Daljeet Gill BA(Hons)

Daljeet is the Head of Design & Development for Pooleys Flight Equipment and editor of the Air Pilot's Manuals, Pre-flight Briefing and R/T Communications as well as many other publications. Daljeet has been involved with the editing, typesetting and designing of all Pooleys publications and products since she joined us in 2001. Graduating in 1999 with a BA(Hons) in Graphic Design, she deals with marketing, advertising, exhibition design and technical design of our manufactured products in the UK. She maintains our website and produces our Pooleys Catalogue. Daljeet's design skills and imaginative approach have brought a new level of clarity and readability to the projects she has touched.

Acknowledgements

Thanks to Jo Shooter and all of my flying colleagues for helping to proof read this book.

Preamble

EASA Part-FCL.120 & 215 requires that applicants for the LAPL(A) and PPL(A) study a course of theoretical knowledge training and pass a theoretical knowledge examination in nine subjects, which is an increase on previous legislation.

The aim of this manual is to provide the required material to study for, and pass, the EASA Part-FCL LAPL(A) and PPL(A) Operational Procedures theoretical knowledge examination. The subject matter covered in Operational Procedures is common to other subjects in both the LAPL(A) and PPL(A) syllabus; therefore, it is recommended that this exam be taken once all of the other series of Air Pilot Manuals have been studied.

INTENTIONALLY BLANK

Chapter 1

OPERATION OF AIRCRAFT

Definitions

The following summarises definitions used in the ICAO Annexes pertinent to EASA Part-FCL. You should be familiar with these definitions because they are used in the PPL examinations. Not every definition has been included as they are not appropriate for PPL operations. The full list is contained in ICAO Annex Operation of Aircraft Part 2.

Acts of Unlawful Interference. These are acts or attempted acts such as to jeopardise the safety of civil aviation and air transport, i.e:

i. Unlawful seizure of aircraft in flight,
ii. Unlawful seizure of aircraft on the ground,
iii. Hostage-taking on board an aircraft or on aerodromes,
iv. Forcible intrusion on board an aircraft, at an airport or on the premises of an aeronautical facility,
v. Introduction on board an aircraft or at an airport of a weapon or hazardous device or material intended for criminal purposes,
vi. Communication of false information as to jeopardise the safety of an aircraft in flight or on the ground, of passengers, crew, ground personnel or the general public, at an airport or on the premises of a civil aviation facility.

Aerial Work. An aircraft operation in which an aircraft is used for specialised services such as agriculture, construction, photography, surveying, observation and patrol, search and rescue, aerial advertisement, etc.

Note. — that the UK definition of aerial work means any purpose, other than commercial air transport or public transport, for which an aircraft is flown if valuable consideration is given or promised for the flight or the purpose of the flight.

Aerodrome. A defined area on land or water (including any buildings, installations and equipment) intended to be used either wholly or in part for the arrival, departure and surface movement of aircraft.

Aerodrome Operating Minima (AOM). The limits of usability of an aerodrome for:

a.   Take-off, expressed in terms of runway visual range and/or visibility and, if necessary, cloud conditions;
b.   Landing in precision approach and landing operations, expressed in terms of visibility and/or runway visual range and decision altitude/height (DA/H) as appropriate to the category of the operation;
c.   Landing in approach and landing operations with vertical guidance, expressed in terms of visibility and/or runway visual range and decision altitude/height (DA/H); and
d.   Landing in non-precision approach and landing operations, expressed in terms of visibility and/or runway visual range, minimum descent altitude/height (MDA/H) and, if necessary, cloud conditions.

Aeroplane. A power-driven heavier-than-air aircraft, deriving its lift in flight chiefly from aerodynamic reactions on surfaces which remain fixed under given conditions of flight.

Aircraft. Any machine that can derive support in the atmosphere from the reactions of the air other than the reactions of the air against the earth's surface.

Aircraft Operating Manual. An operator should provide operations staff and flight crew with an aircraft operating manual, for each aircraft type operated, containing the normal, abnormal and emergency procedures relating to the operation of the aircraft. The manual should be consistent with the aircraft flight manual and checklists to be used. The design of the manual should observe Human Factors principles.

Airworthy. The status of an aircraft, engine, propeller or part when it conforms to its approved design and is in a condition for safe operation.

Alternate Aerodrome. An aerodrome to which an aircraft may proceed when it becomes either impossible or inadvisable to proceed to or to land at the aerodrome of intended landing where the necessary services and facilities are available, where aircraft performance requirements can be met and which is operational at the expected time of use. Alternate aerodromes include the following:

Take-off Alternate. An alternate aerodrome at which an aircraft would be able to land should this become necessary shortly after take-off and it is not possible to use the aerodrome of departure.

En-route Alternate. An alternate aerodrome at which an aircraft would be able to land in the event that a diversion becomes necessary while en route.

Destination Alternate. An alternate aerodrome at which an aircraft would be able to land should it become either impossible or inadvisable to land at the aerodrome of intended landing.

> *Note.* — The aerodrome from which a flight departs may also be an en-route or a destination alternate aerodrome for that flight.

Area Navigation (RNAV). A method of navigation which permits aircraft operation on any desired flight path within the coverage of ground or space-based navigation aids or within the limits of the capability of self-contained aids, or a combination of these.

> *Note.* — Area navigation includes performance-based navigation as well as other operations that do not meet the definition of performance-based navigation.

Commercial Air Transport Operation. An aircraft operation involving the transport of passengers, cargo or mail for remuneration or hire.

Continuing Airworthiness. The set of processes by which an aircraft, engine, propeller or part complies with the applicable airworthiness requirements and remains in a condition for safe operation throughout its operating life.

1

Corporate Aviation Operation. The non-commercial operation or use of aircraft by a company for the carriage of passengers or goods as an aid to the conduct of company business, flown by a professional pilot(s) employed to fly the aircraft.

Dangerous Goods. Articles or substances which are capable of posing a risk to health, safety, property or the environment and which are shown in the list of dangerous goods in the Technical Instructions or which are classified according to those Instructions.

Note. — Dangerous goods are classified in ICAO Annex 18, Chapter 3.

Emergency Locator Transmitter (ELT). A generic term describing equipment which broadcasts distinctive signals on designated frequencies and, depending on application, may be automatically activated by impact or be manually activated. An ELT may be any of the following:

Automatic Fixed ELT (ELT(AF)). An automatically activated ELT which is permanently attached to an aircraft.

Automatic Portable ELT (ELT(AP)). An automatically activated ELT which is rigidly attached to an aircraft but readily removable from the aircraft.

Automatic Deployable ELT (ELT(AD)). An ELT which is rigidly attached to an aircraft and which is automatically deployed and activated by impact, and, in some cases, also by hydrostatic sensors. Manual deployment is also provided.

Survival ELT (ELT(S)). An ELT which is removable from an aircraft, stowed so as to facilitate its ready use in an emergency, and manually activated by survivors.

Engine. A unit used or intended to be used for aircraft propulsion. It consists of at least those components and equipment necessary for functioning and control, but excludes the propeller/rotors (if applicable).

Enhanced Vision System (EVS). A system to display electronic real-time images of the external scene achieved through the use of image sensors.

Extended Flight over Water. A flight operated over water at a distance of more than 93 km (50 NM), or 30 minutes at normal cruising speed, whichever is the lesser, away from land suitable for making an emergency landing.

1

Flight Crew Member. A licensed crew member charged with duties essential to the operation of an aircraft during a flight duty period.

Flight Manual. A manual, associated with the certificate of airworthiness, containing limitations within which the aircraft is to be considered airworthy, and instructions and information necessary to the flight crew members for the safe operation of the aircraft.

Flight Plan. Specified information provided to air traffic services units, relative to an intended flight or portion of a flight of an aircraft.

Flight Recorder. Any type of recorder installed in the aircraft for the purpose of complementing accident/incident investigation.

Flight Simulation Training Device (FSTD). Any one of the following three types of apparatus in which flight conditions are simulated on the ground:

A Flight Simulator, which provides an accurate representation of the flight deck of a particular aircraft type to the extent that the mechanical, electrical, electronic, etc. aircraft systems control functions, the normal environment of flight crew members, and the performance and flight characteristics of that type of aircraft are realistically simulated;

A Flight Procedures Trainer, which provides a realistic flight deck environment, and which simulates instrument responses, simple control functions of mechanical, electrical, electronic, etc. aircraft systems, and the performance and flight characteristics of aircraft of a particular class;

A Basic Instrument Flight Trainer, which is equipped with appropriate instruments, and which simulates the flight deck environment of an aircraft in flight in instrument flight conditions.

Flight Time — Aeroplanes. The total time from the moment an aeroplane first moves for the purpose of taking off until the moment it finally comes to rest at the end of the flight.

> *Note. — Flight time as here defined is synonymous with the term "block to block" time or "chock to chock" time in general usage which is measured from the time an aeroplane first moves for the purpose of taking off until it finally stops at the end of the flight.*

General Aviation Operation. An aircraft operation other than a commercial air transport operation or an aerial work operation.

Head-Up Display (HUD). A display system that presents flight information into the pilot's forward external field of view.

Instrument Meteorological Conditions (IMC). Meteorological conditions expressed in terms of visibility, distance from cloud, and ceiling, less than the minima specified for visual meteorological conditions.

Large Aeroplane. An aeroplane of a maximum certificated take-off mass of over 5700 kg.

Maintenance. The performance of tasks required to ensure the continuing airworthiness of an aircraft, including any one or combination of overhaul, inspection, replacement, defect rectification, and the embodiment of a modification or repair.

Maintenance Programme. A document which describes the specific scheduled maintenance tasks and their frequency of completion and related procedures, such as a reliability programme, necessary for the safe operation of those aircraft to which it applies.

Maintenance Release. A document which contains a certification confirming that the maintenance work to which it relates has been completed in a satisfactory manner, either in accordance with the approved data and the procedures described in the maintenance organisation's procedures manual or under an equivalent system.

Meteorological Information. Meteorological report, analysis, forecast, and any other statement relating to existing or expected meteorological conditions.

Night. The hours between the end of evening civil twilight and the beginning of morning civil twilight or such other period between sunset and sunrise, as may be prescribed by the appropriate authority.

Note. — Civil twilight ends in the evening when the centre of the sun's disc is 6 degrees below the horizon and begins in the morning when the centre of the sun's disc is 6 degrees below the horizon.

1

Operational Flight Plan. The operator's plan for the safe conduct of the flight based on considerations of aeroplane performance, other operating limitations and relevant expected conditions on the route to be followed and at the aerodromes concerned.

Operations Manual. A manual containing procedures, instructions and guidance for use by operational personnel in the execution of their duties.

Operator. A person, organisation or enterprise engaged in or offering to engage in an aircraft operation.

Pilot-in-Command. The pilot designated by the operator or the owner as being in command and charged with the safe conduct of a flight.

Psychoactive Substances. Alcohol, opioids, cannabinoids, sedatives and hypnotics, cocaine, other psychostimulants, hallucinogens, and volatile solvents; whereas coffee and tobacco are excluded.

Repair. The restoration of an aeronautical product to an airworthy condition to ensure that the aircraft continues to comply with the design aspects of the appropriate airworthiness requirements used for the issuance of the type certificate for the respective aircraft type, after it has been damaged or subjected to wear.

Runway Visual Range (RVR). The range over which the pilot of an aircraft on the centre line of a runway can see the runway surface markings or the lights delineating the runway or identifying its centre line.

Safety Management System. A systematic approach to managing safety, including the necessary organisational structures, accountabilities, policies and procedures.

State of Registry. The State on whose register the aircraft is entered.

Visual Meteorological Conditions (VMC). Meteorological conditions expressed in terms of visibility, distance from cloud, and ceiling, equal to or better than specified minima.

1

The following summarises terms used in the ICAO Annexes used in EASA Part-FCL. Whilst it is clearly impossible to memorise all of these terms you should at least be familiar with them as you will be asked questions on them in the theoretical knowledge exam. Typical questions asked are found in Chapter 1 Questions.

ICAO ANNEX TERMINOLOGY

Accident

Event associated with the operation of an aircraft in which the aircraft sustains significant damage, causes significant damage, or causes personal injury. Specifically, an event that occurs between the time any person boards the aircraft with the intention of flight and the time all persons have disembarked, where:

- *a person is fatally or seriously injured as a result of:*
  - *being in the aircraft; or*
  - *being in direct contact with any part of the aircraft, including parts that have fallen off the aircraft; or*
  - *direct exposure to jet blast;*

Note: *Exceptions are when the injuries are from natural causes, self-inflicted or inflicted by other persons, or when the injuries are to stowaways hiding outside the areas normally available to passengers and crew (such as cargo bays).*

- *the aircraft sustains damage or structural failure which:*
  - *jeopardises the structural strength, performance or flight characteristics of the aircraft; or*
  - *would normally require major repair or replacement of the affected component;*

Note: *Exceptions are engine failure or damage (when the damage is limited to the engine, its cowlings or accessories), damage limited to propellers, wing tips, antennae, tyres, brakes, fairings, small dents or puncture holes in the aircraft skin.*

- *the aircraft is missing or is completely inaccessible.*

Note: *An aircraft is considered to be missing when the official search has been terminated and the wreckage has not been found.*

Advisory airspace

Airspace of defined dimensions, or a designated route, within which air traffic advisory service is available.

Advisory route

Designated route along which air traffic advisory service is available.

Aerial work

Aircraft operations where aircraft are used for specialised purposes, such as agriculture, construction, fish-spotting, photography, surveying, search and rescue etc.

Aerodrome

Defined area of land or water used for the arrival, departure and surface movement of aircraft.

1

ICAO ANNEX TERMINOLOGY

Aerodrome beacon
An aeronautical beacon used to indicate the location of an aerodrome from the air.

Aerodrome control service
Air traffic control service for aerodrome traffic.

Aerodrome control tower
A unit established to provide air traffic control services to aerodrome traffic.

Aerodrome elevation
The elevation (height above sea level) of the highest point of the landing area at the aerodrome.

Aerodrome identification sign
A sign at an aerodrome that indicates the name of the aerodrome from the air.

Aerodrome reference point
Designated geographical location of an aerodrome.

Aerodrome traffic
All traffic on the manoeuvring area of an aerodrome and all aircraft flying in the vicinity of an aerodrome.

Note: An aircraft is considered to be 'in the vicinity of an aerodrome' when it is in, entering, or leaving an aerodrome traffic circuit.

Aerodrome traffic circuit
The specified path to be flown by aircraft operating in the vicinity of an aerodrome.

Aeronautical beacon
An aeronautical ground light visible from all directions, either continuously or intermittently, to indicate the location of a particular point on the surface of the earth.

Aeronautical fixed service (AFS)
A telecommunication service between specified fixed points provided primarily for the safety of air navigation and for the regular, efficient and economical operation of air services.

Aeronautical ground light
A light provided to aid air navigation (not a light on an aircraft).

Aeronautical Information Publication (AIP)
A document issued by a State that contains permanent aeronautical information essential to air navigation.

Aeronautical station
A land (or sea) station in the aeronautical mobile service.

Aeronautical telecommunication service
A telecommunication service provided for any aeronautical purpose.

Aeroplane
A power-driven heavier-than-air aircraft that derives its lift from aerodynamic reactions on fixed aerofoils, i.e. fixed-wing.

Airborne collision avoidance system (ACAS)
Aircraft system based on secondary surveillance radar (SSR) transponder signals which indicates to a pilot potential conflicting aircraft that are equipped with SSR transponders. ACAS operates independently of any ground-based equipment.

ICAO ANNEX TERMINOLOGY

Aircraft
Any machine that can support itself in the atmosphere, by means other than the reactions of air against the earth's surface.

Aircraft identification
A group of letters, numbers or a combination thereof which makes up the callsign of an aircraft.

Aircraft observation
A meteorological observation made from an aircraft in flight.

Aircraft proximity
A situation where minimum safe separation distances between aircraft in flight have been compromised.

Aircraft stand
A designated area on an aerodrome apron for the parking of aircraft.

Air-ground communication
Two-way radio communication between aircraft in flight and ground (or sea) stations.

AIRMET information
Information issued by a met office about weather conditions or expected weather conditions that may affect the safety of aircraft. Such information is in addition to previously issued forecasts.

AIRPROX
Code word used in an air traffic incident report to designate aircraft proximity.

Airship
A power-driven lighter-than-air aircraft.

Air-report
A report from an aircraft in flight containing specific information on position, operation and meteorological conditions.

Air-taxiing
Movement of a helicopter above the surface of an aerodrome, normally in ground effect and at a groundspeed of less than 20 knots.

Air traffic
All aircraft in flight or operating on the manoeuvring areas of aerodromes.

Air traffic advisory service
A service provided within advisory airspace to ensure separation in so far as practical between aircraft operating on IFR flight plans.

Air traffic control clearance
Authorisation for an aircraft to proceed under conditions specified by an air traffic control unit. This term is often abbreviated to 'clearance'.

Air traffic control instruction
A directive issued by air traffic control that requires a pilot to take a specific action.

Air traffic control service
A service provided (a) to expedite the flow of air traffic and (b) to prevent collisions between aircraft in flight and on the manoeuvring area, and between aircraft and ground obstructions.

Air traffic control unit
Aerodrome control tower, area control centre or approach control office.

ICAO ANNEX TERMINOLOGY

Air traffic service
Flight information service, alerting service, air traffic advisory service or air traffic control service.

Air traffic services airspaces
Airspaces of defined dimensions, alphabetically designated (Classes A to G), within which specific types of flights may operate and for which specific air traffic services and rules of operation apply.

Air traffic services unit
Air traffic control unit, flight information centre or air traffic services reporting office.

Airway
A corridor-shaped control area equipped with radio navigation aids.

Alerting service
Service which notifies appropriate organisations of aircraft that require search and rescue aid.

Alert phase
Where concern is registered regarding the safety of an aircraft and its occupants.

Alternate aerodrome
An aerodrome to which an aircraft may proceed if it becomes either impossible or inadvisable to proceed to or land at the intended destination aerodrome. Alternate aerodromes include the following:

- En-route alternate: an aerodrome at which an aircraft would be able to land after experiencing an abnormal or emergency condition while en route.

- Destination alternate: an alternate aerodrome to which an aircraft may proceed if it becomes either impossible or inadvisable to land at the intended destination aerodrome.

Note: The departure aerodrome may also be an en-route or destination alternate aerodrome for the flight.

Altitude
The vertical distance of a point from mean sea level.

Approach control office
A unit established to provide air traffic control service to controlled flights arriving at, or departing from, one or more aerodromes.

Approach control service
Air traffic control service for arriving or departing controlled flights.

Approach sequence
The order in which two or more aircraft are cleared to approach to land at an aerodrome.

Appropriate ATS authority
The authority designated by a State as being responsible for providing air traffic services in its territory.

Appropriate authority
(a) Regarding flight over the high seas: the relevant authority of the State of Registry; (b) Regarding flight over the territory of a State: the relevant authority of the State that has sovereignty over the territory being overflown.

Apron
An area on an aerodrome where aircraft can be parked for the loading and unloading of passengers, mail or cargo, refuelling or maintenance.

1

ICAO ANNEX TERMINOLOGY

Area control centre
Unit which provides air traffic control service to controlled flights in control areas under its jurisdiction.

Area control service
Air traffic control service for controlled flights in control areas.

Area navigation (RNAV)
A navigation method where aircraft may operate on any flightpath within the coverage of station-referenced navigation aids or within the limits of self-contained aids, or both. Such systems avoid the need to overfly ground-based radio navigation aids.

Area navigation route
An ATS route for aircraft using area navigation.

Assignment, assign
Distribution of frequencies to stations or SSR codes to aircraft.

ATIS
Automatic terminal information service: continuous repetitive broadcast of current routine aerodrome information to arriving and departing aircraft.

ATS route
A route (airway, advisory route, arrival or departure route etc.) used as necessary for the provision of air traffic services.

Balloon
A non-power-driven lighter-than-air aircraft.

Blind transmission
A radio transmission from one station to another where the transmitter cannot hear the receiver, but believes that the transmission can be received.

Broadcast
An 'all stations' transmission of air navigation information.

Ceiling
The height above ground or water of the lowest layer of cloud below 20,000 ft covering more than half the sky.

Clearance limit
The point to which an aircraft is granted an air traffic control clearance.

Clearway
A defined rectangular area at the upwind end of a runway that is suitable for the initial climb-out of aeroplanes. Will be under the control of the aerodrome authority.

Control area
A controlled airspace extending upwards from a specified height above the earth's surface.

Controlled aerodrome
An aerodrome at which a control service to aircraft is provided.

Note: This does not necessarily imply that the aircraft is within a control zone.

Controlled airspace
An airspace of defined dimensions within which air traffic control services are provided to IFR and VFR flights.

1

ICAO ANNEX TERMINOLOGY

Controlled flight
Any flight subject to air traffic control clearances.

Control zone
A controlled airspace extending upwards from the earth's surface to a specified upper limit.

Cruise climb
An aeroplane cruising technique resulting in a net gain in altitude as the aeroplane mass decreases.

Cruising level
A level maintained during a significant portion of a flight.

Dangerous goods
Articles or substances that are capable of posing significant risk to health, safety or property when they are transported by air.

Declared distances
Declared distances at aerodromes are agreed by the relevant authority – in the UK this is the CAA, and the distances are published in the Aerodrome section of the AIP.

- **Take-off run available (TORA).** The length of runway declared available and suitable for the ground run of an aeroplane taking off.

- **Take-off distance available (TODA).** The length of the take-off run available plus the length of the clearway, if provided.

- **Accelerate-stop distance available (ASDA).** The length of the take-off run available plus the length of the stopway, if provided.

- **Landing distance available (LDA).** The length of runway declared available and suitable for the ground run of an aeroplane landing.

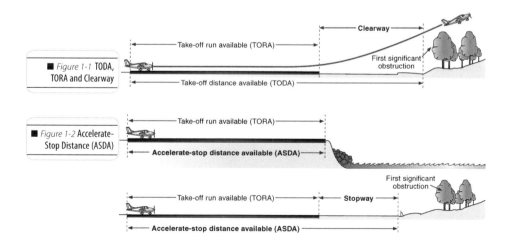

■ *Figure 1-1* **TODA, TORA and Clearway**

■ *Figure 1-2* **Accelerate-Stop Distance (ASDA)**

1

ICAO ANNEX TERMINOLOGY

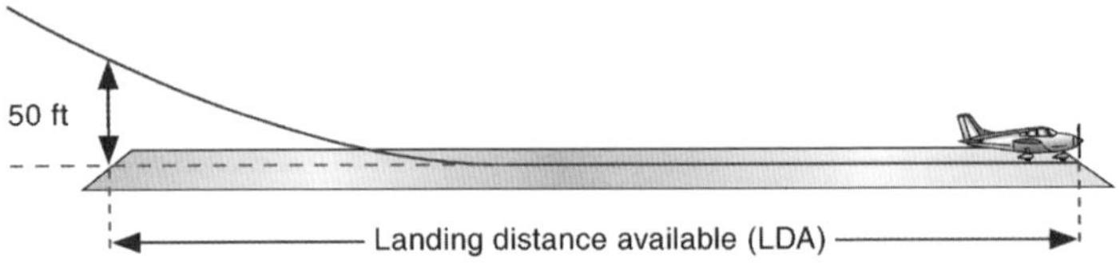

50 ft

Landing distance available (LDA)

■ *Figure 1-3* Landing Distance Available (LDA)

Distress phase
Where it is reasonably certain that an aircraft and its occupants require immediate assistance or are threatened by grave or imminent danger.

Ditching
The forced landing of an aircraft on water.

Elevation
The vertical distance between a point on the earth's surface and mean sea level.

Emergency phase
Generic term meaning either uncertainty phase, alert phase or distress phase.

Estimated elapsed time
Estimated time required to proceed from one significant point to another.

Estimated off-block time
Estimated time at which the aircraft will move 'off chocks' to begin movement towards take-off.

Estimated time of arrival (ETA)
For VFR flights, the estimated time at which the aircraft will arrive over the destination aerodrome.
For IFR flights, the estimated time at which the aircraft will arrive over a point defined by radio navigation aids, from which an instrument approach procedure will begin

(if the destination aerodrome does not have an associated navigation aid, ETA is the time at which the aircraft will arrive over the aerodrome).

Expected approach time
The time at which ATC expects an arriving aircraft that has been instructed to hold will leave the holding pattern to complete its approach for a landing.

Filed flight plan
A flight plan as submitted to an ATS unit without subsequent changes.

Fireproof material
A material capable of withstanding heat as well as, or better than, steel

Flight crew member
A licensed crew member charged with duties essential to the operation of an aircraft during flight.

Flight Information centre
A unit that provides flight information service and alerting service.

Flight information region
An airspace of defined dimensions within which flight information service and alerting service is provided.

Flight information service
Service which provides advice and information useful to the safe and efficient conduct of flights.

1

ICAO ANNEX TERMINOLOGY

Flight level
A surface of constant atmospheric pressure which is related to a specific pressure datum, 1013.2 mb (hPa), and is separated from other such surfaces by specific pressure intervals. Flight levels are expressed in hundreds of feet, e.g. FL180 = 18,000 ft.

Flight Manual
A manual, associated with the Certificate of Airworthiness, containing limitations within which the aircraft is to be considered airworthy, and instructions and information necessary to the pilot for the safe operation of the aircraft. An aircraft Flight Manual is written by the manufacturer (e.g. Piper), approved by the State of Manufacture (in the US approval is given by the FAA) and supplemented if necessary by the State of Registration (for instance, by the UK CAA). The Flight Manual forms part of the Certificate of Airworthiness.

Flight plan
Specified information provided to air traffic services units about an intended flight or portion of a flight.

Flight time
The total time from the beginning of the take-off roll until the moment the aircraft stops at the end of a flight.

Note: This definition of flight time is synonymous with the terms 'block to block' or 'chock to chock'.

Flight visibility
Visibility forward from the cockpit of an aircraft in flight.

Forecast
A description of the expected weather conditions over a specified period of time for a particular area.

General aviation operation
An aircraft operation other than a commercial air transport flight or an aerial work operation.

Glider
A non-power-driven heavier-than-air aircraft that derives its lift from aerodynamic reactions on fixed aerofoils.

Ground visibility
Visibility at an aerodrome, as reported by a meteorological observer.

Gyroplane
A power-driven heavier-than-air rotorcraft that derives its lift from aerodynamic reactions on a freely-rotating rotor in the vertical axis. Powered by a propeller on the longitudinal axis.

Hazard beacon
An aeronautical beacon used to indicate a danger to air navigation.

Heading
The direction in which an aircraft is pointing, usually expressed in degrees from north (either true, magnetic or compass).

Height
The vertical distance between a point and a specified datum (such as sea level or ground level).

Heavier-than-air aircraft
An aircraft that derives its lift mainly from aerodynamic forces.

1

ICAO ANNEX TERMINOLOGY

Helicopter
A heavier-than-air rotorcraft that derives its lift and control from one or more power-driven rotors on substantially vertical axes.

Heliport
An aerodrome or a defined area on a structure for the landing, taking off and surface movement of helicopters.

Holding bay
A defined area at an aerodrome where aircraft can be held or bypassed without disrupting the flow of other traffic.

Holding point
A specified location, around which an aircraft flies a standard pattern until cleared to proceed with the flight.

Identification beacon
An aeronautical beacon that flashes a coded signal such that its location can be identified.

IFR flight
A flight made under the Instrument Flight Rules.

IMC
Instrument Meteorological Conditions.

Incident
An occurrence, other than an accident, which affects or could affect the safety of an aircraft operation.

Instrument Meteorological Conditions (IMC)
Meteorological conditions expressed in terms of visibility, distance from cloud, and ceiling, less than the minima specified for visual meteorological conditions.

Investigation
A process conducted for the purpose of accident investigation which includes the gathering and analysis of information, the drawing of conclusions, including the determination of causes and, when appropriate, the making of safety recommendations.

Landing area
The area on an aerodrome used for the landing or take-off of aircraft.

Level
A generic term relating to the vertical position of an aircraft in flight – referring to either height, altitude or flight level.

Lighter-than-air aircraft
An aircraft that is supported in flight mainly by its buoyancy in the air (e.g. a hot-air balloon).

Location indicator
A four-letter code assigned to the location of an aeronautical fixed station (could be either an aerodrome or a met station).

Manoeuvring area
The part of an aerodrome used for the taxiing, take-off and landing of aircraft, excluding aprons.

Marker
An object displayed above ground level to indicate an obstacle or boundary, e.g. the orange-and-white striped wedge-shaped markers that delineate an aerodrome boundary.

ICAO ANNEX TERMINOLOGY

Marking
A symbol or group of symbols displayed on the surface of the movement area to convey aeronautical information, e.g. the double white cross used to indicate gliding is in progress.

Meteorological information
Meteorological report, analysis, forecast or other statement relating to existing or expected weather conditions.

Meteorological office
An office that provides a meteorological service for international air navigation.

Meteorological report
A statement of observed weather conditions at a specific place at a specific time.

Mode (SSR)
Mode of operation of SSR transponder, e.g. Mode C (altitude reporting) or Mode A.

Movement area
The part of an aerodrome used for the taxiing, take-off and landing of aircraft, including the manoeuvring area and apron(s).

Night
The hours between the end of evening civil twilight and the beginning of morning civil twilight or such other period between sunset and sunrise as may be prescribed by the appropriate aviation authority.

Non-instrument runway
A runway for the use of aircraft using visual approach procedures only.

Non-radar separation
Separation distances between aircraft when position information is obtained from sources other than radar.

NOTAM
Notice to Airmen, which contains urgent information concerning the establishment, condition or change in any aeronautical facility, service, procedure or hazard.

Obstacle
Any fixed or mobile object (or part thereof) located on the surface movement area of an aerodrome that extends above a defined height.

Operator
A person, organisation or enterprise engaged in or offering facilities in aircraft operations.

Pilot-in-command
The pilot responsible for the operation and safety of an aircraft during flight time.

Pressure altitude
An atmospheric pressure expressed in terms of altitude which corresponds to that pressure in the standard atmosphere (i.e. 1013.2 hPa set in altimeter subscale).

Primary radar
Radar system that uses reflected radio signals.

Primary surveillance radar
Radar surveillance system that uses reflected radio signals.

1

ICAO ANNEX TERMINOLOGY

RADAR
Radio detection system which provides information on range, position and elevation of objects.

Radar approach
An approach to land where the final approach phase is directed by a radar controller.

Radar clutter
Unwanted signals displayed on a radar screen, caused by interference, static etc.

Radar contact
When the radar position of a particular aircraft is seen and identified on a radar display.

Radar control
Where radar information is used directly in the provision of air traffic control.

Radar controller
An air traffic controller qualified to use radar information.

Radar display
Electronic display (screen, monitor) which uses radar information to depict the position and movement of aircraft.

Radar identification
When the position of a particular aircraft is seen on a radar display and positively identified by the air traffic controller.

Radar monitoring
Use of radar to provide aircraft with information on their deviations from planned flightpath and deviations from air traffic control clearances.

Radar separation
Separation distances used when aircraft position information is provided by radar sources.

Radar service
A service provided by means of radar.

Radar unit
Part of an air traffic services unit that uses radar.

Radar vectoring
Where a radar controller issues heading instructions to aircraft, based on radar information.

Radio direction-finding station
A radio station that determines the relative direction of other transmitting stations.

Radiotelephony
A form of radio communication used mainly for the exchange of speech information.

Reporting point
A geographic location at which the position of an aircraft in flight can be reported.

Rescue coordination centre
Unit responsible for organising search and rescue operations within a certain area.

Rescue unit
A group of people trained and equipped to perform search and rescue operations.

Rotorcraft
A power-driven heavier-than-air aircraft that is supported in flight by reactions of air on one or more rotors.

1

ICAO ANNEX TERMINOLOGY

Runway
A defined rectangular area on an aerodrome used for the take-off and landing of aircraft.

Runway guard lights
A light system which alerts pilots or vehicle drivers that they are about to enter an active runway.

Runway visual range (RVR)
The distance along which the pilot of an aircraft on the centre-line of a runway can see the runway surface markings or lights.

Safety recommendation
A proposal made by the accident investigation authority of the State conducting an investigation, based on information derived from the investigation, with the intention of preventing accidents or incidents.

Search and rescue aircraft
An aircraft equipped to conduct search and rescue missions.

Search and rescue region
An area of defined dimensions within which search and rescue service is provided.

Search and rescue services unit
A generic term meaning either rescue coordination centre, rescue subcentre or alerting post.

Secondary radar
Radar system where an 'interrogating' radio signal transmitted from the radar station prompts a 'reply' signal to be sent from an aircraft transponder.

Secondary surveillance radar (SSR)
Radar system that uses transmitters/receivers (interrogators) and transponders.

Serious incident
An event that almost resulted in an accident.

Note: The only difference between an accident and an incident is the result: damage and/or injury = accident; could have been damage and/or injury = incident.

Serious injury
An injury sustained by a person in an accident which:

- requires hospitalisation for more than 48 hours (from within 7 days of the accident);
- results in a bone fracture (apart from simple fractures of fingers, toes or nose);
- involves lacerations which cause severe haemorrhage, nerve, muscle or tendon damage;
- involves injury to any internal organ;
- involves second or third degree burns, or any burns that affect more than 5% of body surface;
- involves verified exposure to infectious substances or harmful radiation.

SIGMET information
Information issued by a met office concerning weather conditions or expected weather conditions that may affect the safety of flights.

Signal area
An area on an aerodrome used for the display of ground signals.

1

ICAO ANNEX TERMINOLOGY

Slush
Water-saturated snow which, with a heel-and-toe slap-down motion against the ground, will be displaced with a splatter.

Snow (on the ground)

- **Dry snow.** Snow which can be blown if loose or, if compacted by hand, will fall apart again on release.

- **Wet snow.** Snow which, if compacted by hand, will stick together and tend to form a snowball.

- **Compacted snow.** Snow which has been compressed into a solid mass that resists further compression and will hold together or break into lumps if picked up.

Special VFR flight
A VFR flight cleared by air traffic control to operate within a control zone in meteorological conditions below VMC.

State of Design
The State that has jurisdiction over the organisation responsible for the design of a particular aircraft type.

State of Manufacture
The State that has jurisdiction over the organisation responsible for final assembly of an aircraft.

State of Occurrence
The State in which an aircraft accident or incident occurs.

State of the Operator
The State in which the operator's principal place of business is located, or if there is no such place, the operator's permanent residence.

State of Registry
The State (nation) in which an aircraft is registered.

Stopway
A defined rectangular area on the ground at the end of the take-off end of a runway, prepared as a suitable area in which an aeroplane can stop in the case of an abandoned take-off.

Surveillance radar
Radar equipment used to determine the range and position of aircraft in azimuth.

Take-off runway
A runway intended for take-off only.

Taxi-holding position
A designated position at an aerodrome where taxiing aircraft may be required to hold before entering or crossing a runway.

Taxiing
Movement on the surface of an aerodrome of an aircraft under its own power, excluding take-off and landing.

Taxiway
A defined path on an aerodrome for the taxiing of aircraft.

Terminal control area
A control area normally established around a major aerodrome.

Threshold
The beginning of the usable portion of a runway (normally indicated by 'piano key' markings).

ICAO ANNEX TERMINOLOGY

Touchdown zone
The portion of a runway, beyond the threshold, where it is intended landing aeroplanes first contact the runway.

Track
The path of an aircraft in flight over the earth's surface.

Traffic avoidance advice
Advice given by air traffic control to pilots to assist in collision avoidance.

Traffic information
Information given by air traffic control to pilots regarding other known traffic near or on the flight-planned route.

Transition altitude
The altitude at or below which the vertical position of aircraft is controlled by reference to altitudes (i.e. with Regional QNH set). Transition altitudes vary considerably between countries: 3,000 ft in the UK, 18,000 ft in the USA.

Transition layer
Airspace between the transition altitude and transition level.

Transition level
The lowest flight level available for use above the transition altitude.

Uncertainty phase
When the safety of an aircraft and its occupants is uncertain.

VFR flight
Flight conducted under the Visual Flight Rules.

Visibility
The distance over which prominent unlighted objects by day and prominent lighted objects by night can be seen.

Visual approach
An approach to land by an IFR flight where part or all of an instrument approach procedure is not completed and the approach is conducted by visual reference to terrain.

Visual meteorological conditions
Meteorological conditions expressed in terms of visibility, distance from cloud, and ceiling, equal or better than specified minima.

VMC
Visual meteorological conditions.

Waypoint
A specific geographical location used by an area navigation system.

1

Applicability

The Standards and Recommended Practices contained in Annex 6, Part II, sections 2 and 3, shall be applicable to international general aviation operations in aeroplanes.

Note. — 1 Standards and Recommended Practices applicable to the operation of aeroplanes by operators authorised to conduct international commercial air transport operations are to be found in Annex 6, Part I.

Note. — 2 Standards and Recommended Practices applicable to international commercial air transport operations or international general aviation operations with helicopters are to be found in Annex 6, Part III.

Note. — 3 Section 2 of Annex 6, Part II, applies to all international general aviation aeroplane operations, including those covered in Section 3. Section 3 adds additional requirements for large aeroplanes, turbojet aeroplanes and corporate aviation operations.

ICAO Annex 6, General Requirements

International Flights (ICAO Annex 6)

The following extracts from Annex 6 cover matters particularly relevant to PPL holders making international flights.

GENERAL

3.1.   The pilot-in-command shall comply with the relevant laws, regulations and procedures of the States in which the aircraft is operated.

3.2.   The pilot-in-command shall be responsible for the operation and safety of the aeroplane and for the safety of all persons on board, during the flight.

3.3.   Should an emergency situation occur which endangers the safety of the aeroplane or people, and requires the pilot to take action which violates local regulations or procedures, the pilot shall notify the appropriate authority as soon as possible. Some States may require the pilot to submit a report on the violation, normally within ten days.

3.4.   In the event of an accident involving the aeroplane which results in serious injury or death or substantial damage to the aeroplane or property the pilot-in-command shall be responsible for notifying the appropriate authority as quickly as possible.

3.5.   ICAO recommends that the pilot-in-command should carry on board the aeroplane essential information on search and rescue services in the areas over which the aeroplane will be flown.

ADEQUACY OF OPERATING FACILITIES

4.1.   The pilot-in-command shall not begin a flight unless he has ascertained that the aerodrome facilities, communication facilities and navigation aids required are adequate for the safe operation of the aeroplane.

AERODROME OPERATING MINIMA

4.2.   The pilot-in-command shall not fly below the operating minima specified for an aerodrome, except with State approval.

1

BRIEFING

4.3.1   The pilot-in-command shall ensure that crew members and passengers are briefed on the location and use of:

- seat belts;
- emergency exits;
- life jackets;
- oxygen equipment;
- any other emergency equipment, including passenger briefing cards.

4.3.2   The pilot-in-command shall ensure that everyone on board is familiar with the location and use of emergency equipment carried for collective use, such as life rafts.

AEROPLANE AIRWORTHINESS AND SAFETY PRECAUTIONS

4.4.1   The pilot-in-command shall not begin a flight unless he is satisfied that:

- the aeroplane is airworthy, registered and has the appropriate certificates on board;
- the instruments and equipment in the aircraft are appropriate to the expected flight conditions;
- necessary maintenance has been completed;
- the aeroplane's weight and balance will be within safe limits for the flight;
- cargo is correctly stowed and secured;
- the aeroplane's operating limitations, as described in the Flight Manual, will not be exceeded.

NOTE: ICAO recommends that the pilot-in-command should have sufficient information on climb performance to be able to determine the climb gradient that can be achieved during the departure phase in the prevailing conditions.

LIMITATIONS IMPOSED BY WEATHER CONDITIONS

4.6.1   Flights to be conducted under the visual flight rules shall not be commenced unless current weather reports and forecasts indicate that visual meteorological conditions exist along the flight-planned route.

4.6.3   Flights shall not be continued towards the planned destination aerodrome unless current weather reports indicate conditions at that aerodrome, or at least one alternate destination aerodrome, are at or above specified minima.

4.6.4   Aeroplanes on approach to land shall not exceed aerodrome operating minima, except in emergency situations.

4.6.5   A flight may not be conducted in known or expected icing conditions unless the aeroplane is equipped to cope with such conditions.

FUEL AND OIL SUPPLY

4.8.1   A flight may not be commenced unless the aeroplane carries sufficient fuel and oil to complete the flight safely, considering the weather conditions and any expected delays.

IN-FLIGHT EMERGENCY INSTRUCTION

4.11   In an in-flight emergency, the pilot-in-command shall ensure that passengers and crew are instructed in appropriate emergency action.

WEATHER REPORTING BY PILOTS

4.12   If weather conditions are encountered that are likely to affect the safety of other flights, they should be reported as soon as possible.

HAZARDOUS FLIGHT CONDITIONS

4.13   Hazardous flight conditions encountered in-flight such as volcanic ash and dust-storms, other than those associated with weather conditions, should be reported as soon as possible.

INSTRUCTION – GENERAL

4.17.   An aeroplane may be taxied on the movement area of an aerodrome only if the person at the controls:

- has been authorised by the owner, lessee or agent to do so;
- is fully competent to taxy the aeroplane;
- is qualified to use the radio if radio communications are required;
- has received instruction from a competent person in aerodrome layout, routes, signs, marking, lights, ATC signals and instructions, phraseology and procedures and is able to conform safely to the operational standards required for the safe movement of aeroplanes at the aerodrome.

REFUELLING WITH PASSENGERS ON BOARD

4.18.1   ICAO recommends that aircraft should not be refuelled while passengers are boarding, on board, or leaving the aircraft, unless it is attended by the pilot-in-command or another qualified person who is able to organise an evacuation of the aircraft should it be necessary.

AEROPLANE PERFORMANCE AND OPERATING LIMITATIONS

5.1   An aeroplane shall be operated:
- in compliance with its airworthiness certificate;
- within the operating limitations prescribed by the certificating authority of the State of registry.

5.2   Placards, listings and instrument markings containing operating limitations prescribed by the State of registry shall be displayed in the aeroplane.

AEROPLANE INSTRUMENTS AND EQUIPMENT

6.1   In addition to the minimum equipment necessary to satisfy the Certificate of Airworthiness, an aeroplane shall carry the instruments, equipment and documents appropriate to the planned flight.

6.2   An aeroplane shall be equipped with instruments that will enable the flight crew to control the flightpath of the aeroplane, carry out any required procedural manoeuvre, and observe the operating limitations of the aeroplane in the expected flight conditions.

6.1.3   Aeroplanes shall be equipped with:
- an accessible first-aid kit;
- a safe portable fire extinguisher in the cockpit and in each passenger compartment if separate from the cockpit;
- a seat or berth for each person on board over a minimum age determined by the State of registry;
- a seat belt for each seat and restraining belts for each berth;
- the following manuals, charts and information:
  - the Flight Manual and other necessary related documents;
  - suitable aeronautical charts for the planned route and any diversions that could reasonably be anticipated;
  - procedures and visual signals for pilots-in-command of intercepted aircraft (for UK pilots, this is the CAA's General Aviation Safety Sense Leaflet No. 11);
- spare fuses for replacement of those accessible in flight.

1

VFR FLIGHTS

6.2   Aeroplanes operating on VFR flights shall be equipped with:
- a magnetic compass;
- an accurate timepiece that indicates the time in hours, minutes and seconds;
- an altimeter;
- an airspeed indicator;
- additional instruments or equipment that may be prescribed by the appropriate authority.

FLIGHTS OVER WATER

6.3.2   All single-engined landplanes when flying over water beyond gliding distance from land should carry one life-jacket or equivalent flotation device for each person on board, stowed in an easily accessible position for its intended user.

NOTE : *Landplanes above includes amphibious aircraft operated as landplanes.*

6.3.3   All aeroplanes on extended flights over water shall be equipped as follows:
- When over water and more than 50 nautical miles from land suitable for an emergency landing:
  - one life-jacket or equivalent flotation device for each person on board, stowed in an easily accessible position for its intended user.
- When over water and more than 100 nautical miles from land suitable for an emergency landing in the case of single-engined aeroplanes, and more than 200 nautical miles in the case of multi- engined aeroplanes capable of continuing flight with one engine inoperative:
  - live-saving rafts capable of carrying all persons on board, stowed for ready access in an emergency, provided with appropriate life- saving equipment;
  - equipment for making pyrotechnic distress signals.

FLIGHTS OVER DESIGNATED LAND AREAS

6.4   Aeroplanes flying over land areas designated by the State as being areas in which search and rescue would be especially difficult, shall be equipped with appropriate signalling devices and life-saving equipment.

1

Compliance with Laws, Regulations & Procedures

The pilot-in-command (PIC) shall have responsibility for operational control.

PASSENGERS

The pilot-in-command (PIC) shall ensure that, during take-off and landing and whenever considered necessary by reason of turbulence or any emergency occurring during flight, all passengers on board an aeroplane shall be secured in their seats by means of the seat belts or harnesses provided.

FLIGHT PLANNING

A flight shall not be commenced unless, taking into account both the meteorological conditions and any delays that are expected in flight, the aeroplane carries sufficient fuel and oil to ensure that it can safely complete the flight. The amount of fuel to be carried must permit:

a. When the flight is conducted in accordance with the visual flight rules by day, flight to the aerodrome of intended landing, and after that, for at least 30 minutes at normal cruising altitude; or

b. When the flight is conducted in accordance with the visual flight rules by night, flight to the aerodrome of intended landing and thereafter for at least 45 minutes at normal cruising altitude.

Note. — Nothing precludes amendment of a flight plan in flight in order to replan the flight to another aerodrome, provided that the requirements above can be complied with from the point where the flight is replanned.

FLIGHT CREW MEMBERS AT DUTY STATIONS

When operating an aircraft flight crew members should be at the following positions during the flight:

Take-off & Landing. All flight crew members required to be on flight deck duty shall be at their stations.

En route. All flight crew members required to be on flight deck duty shall remain at their stations except when their absence is necessary for the performance of duties in connection with the operation of the aeroplane or for physiological needs.

Seat Belts. All flight crew members shall keep their seat belts fastened when at their stations.

Safety Harness. When safety harnesses are provided, any flight crew member occupying a pilot's seat shall keep the safety harness fastened during the take-off and landing phases; all other flight crew members shall keep their safety harnesses fastened during the take-off and landing phases unless the shoulder straps interfere with the performance of their duties, in which case the shoulder straps may be unfastened but the seat belt must remain fastened.

Note. — Safety harness includes shoulder strap(s) and a seat belt which may be used independently.

AEROPLANE COMMUNICATION AND NAVIGATION EQUIPMENT

An aeroplane to be operated in accordance with the instrument flight rules or at night shall be provided with radio communication equipment. Such equipment shall be capable of conducting two-way communication with those aeronautical stations and on those frequencies prescribed by the appropriate authority. The units should be independent of each other, so that in the event of failure, the remaining unit is still operational.

VFR flights operating within controlled airspace require a radio unless exempt by the appropriate authority.

The radio communication equipment shall provide for communication on the aeronautical emergency frequency 121.5 MHz

---

NOW COMPLETE – CHAPTER 1 QUESTIONS

1

INTENTIONALLY BLANK

Chapter 2

NOISE ABATEMENT PROCEDURES

Noise Abatement Procedures (NAPs) were implemented to reduce the noise footprint of aircraft on the surrounding areas of airfields. Reduction of noise is very important, as the success of an airport is, in part, down to how it integrates with the local community.

Aviation legislation dictates how low above people, vessels and objects an aircraft may fly and if the Commander is found guilty of breaking the Air Navigation Order and Rules of the Air, then the CAA's Regulation Enforcement and Legal departments may seek a prosecution through the Magistrates and Crown Courts.

Although national aviation authorities, government agencies, and the aviation community as a whole recognise the impact that aircraft noise has on the local community living near an airfield, it is not covered by either the Environmental Protection Act 1990, or the Noise Act 1996. This means that local authorities do not have any right to legal action with respect to aircraft noise. If however, a new airport was built, or an existing airport operator wanted to develop their airport (such as building another runway), the local authority could impose operating conditions as part of the planning application and approval process.

The CAA must also consider the environmental noise impact before approving an airspace expansion, however, it can only prosecute if an aircraft has broken one of the low flying rules and it must have sufficient evidence before doing so.

When an airport receives a noise complaint an investigation will be carried out and the circumstances examined. At small airfields it is very difficult to gain sufficient evidence to confirm whether an aircraft did indeed break NAPs. It is often a case of one person's word against another's. If it is concluded that under normal operations a pilot did not comply with an airfield's NAPs then the operator may take action. Although the CAA cannot prosecute for noise impact, airport operators can impose their own penalties to persistent pilots and commercial operators who break Noise Abatement Procedures, examples of which are detailed below:

i.   Verbal briefing from the tower.
ii.   Re-training with a local instructor.
iii. Restrictions on operating times.
iv.   Monetary fine.
v.   In extreme cases, temporary or permanent ban from operating at the airfield.

To avoid these sanctions and friction between the community and the airfield, review the airfield's Noise Preferential Routings and Noise Abatement Procedures at the pre-flight planning stage. Once airborne, contact the destination ATSU early, obtain the airfield information, plan the arrival and approach with reference to NAPs. If you are still in doubt regarding the procedures contact the destination ATSU.

EASA produces a Type-Certificate Data Sheet for Noise (TCDSN) for all aircraft built today and these have to meet noise requirements specified by ICAO. The CAA certifies light aircraft and helicopters through the Aeroplane Noise Regulations 1999, the Aeroplane Noise (Amendment) Regulations 1999 and the Air Navigation (Environmental Standards for Non-EASA Aircraft) Order 2008. Each aircraft is given a Noise Certificate, which remains valid unless the engine or airframe is modified. The Noise Certificate is usually kept in the 'Essential Documents' folder together with the Certificate of Insurance, Certificate of Airworthiness, etc.

In summary:

1.   Legal action cannot be taken against an aircraft for noise emissions, only for breaking the Rules of the Air.
2.   The flying community take their responsibilities towards being good neighbours very seriously.
3.   All aircraft have a noise certificate, which remains valid, unless engine or airframe modifications take place.
4.   Airfield operators can impose their own penalties for NAP offenders.

Figure 2-1 Noise Certificate

1. State of registry	3. Document Number:
UNITED KINGDOM	019537
2. NOISE CERTIFICATE	

4. Registration Marks:	5. Manufacturer and Manufacturer's Designation of Aircraft:	6. Aircraft Serial Number:
G-JDBC	PIPER AIRCRAFT CORPORATION PIPER PA-34-200T	34-7570150

7. Engine:	8. Propeller:
CONTINENTAL MOTORS CORP TSIO-360-E	HARTZELL BHC-C2YF-2CKUF/FC8459-8R

9. Maximum Take-Off Mass (kg)	10. Maximum Landing Mass (kg)	11. Noise Certification Standard:
1999	Not Applicable	Chapter 6

12. Additional modifications incorporated for the purpose of compliance with the applicable noise certification standards:

None

13. Lateral/Full-Power Noise Level:	14. Approach Noise Level:	15. Flyover Noise Level:	16. Overflight Noise Level:	17. Take-Off Noise Level:
N/A	N/A	N/A	71.7 dB(A)	N/A

Remarks:

None

18. This Noise Certificate is issued pursuant to Annex 16, Volume I to the Convention on International Civil Aviation dated 7 December 1944 and Regulation (EC) No. 216/2008, Article 6 in respect of the above-mentioned aircraft, which is considered to comply with the indicated noise standard when maintained and operated in accordance with the relevant requirements and operating limitations.

19. Date of Issue........10 December 2008............   20. Signature...........................

EASA Form 45 18042008

Influence of the Flight Procedure (Departure, Cruise and Approach)

Noise Abatement Procedures (NAPs) for large turboprop or turbojet aircraft combine a reduction in thrust with a departure route, which reduces noise ground pattern to a minimum. Noise sensors are positioned on the departure route and operators who do not reduce thrust or follow the tracks accurately are fined. ICAO PANS-OPS defines two types of Noise Abatement Departure Procedures (NADPS) often referred to as NADP1 and NADP2, which you may read in the Noise Abatement Procedures section of applicable aerodrome entry in the AIP.

■ Figure 2-2 Noise Abatement Sensor Locations, which monitor compliance with NAPs.

JEPPESEN
JeppView 3.7.2.1

EGSS/STN
STANSTED

JEPPESEN
23 APR 10 (30-4) **Eff 6 May**

LONDON, UK
NOISE

| Apt Elev 348' | NOISE ABATEMENT |

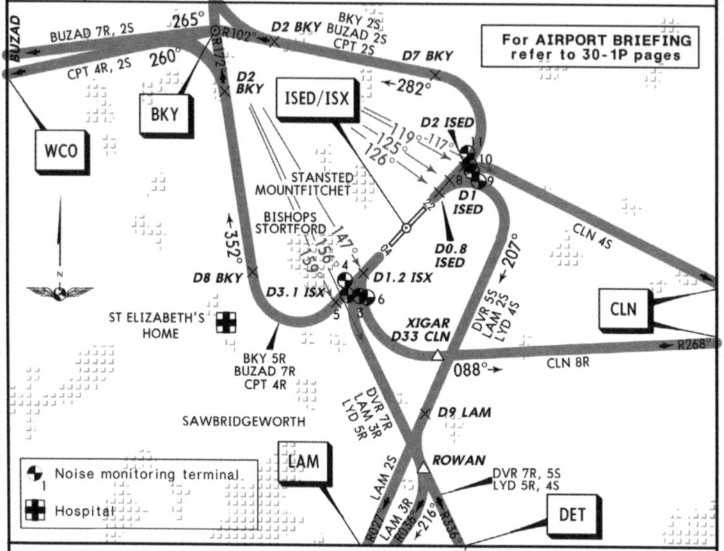

For AIRPORT BRIEFING
refer to 30-1P pages

The operation limits as specified in para 3.1.1. (refer to Airport Briefing Page 30-1P5) shall be adjusted in respect of any noise monitoring terminal to take account of the location and its ground elevation relative to the aerodrome elevation as follows:

	NOISE MONITORING TERMINAL/NAME/LOCATION		ELEVATION ABOVE AERODROME	ADJUSTMENT db(A)
◐₃	Howe Green School, Great Hallingbury	N51 50.8 E000 11.5	- 21m	- 1.0
◐₄	Thames Water, Bishop's Stortford	N51 51.3 E000 10.7	- 36m	- 1.4
◐₅	Woolcott Restaurant, Great Hallingbury	N51 50.9 E000 10.9	- 26m	- 1.4
◐₆	Morley, Woodside Green	N51 50.8 E000 11.9	- 26m	- 1.1
◐₈	Anglian Water, Broxted	N51 54.9 E000 17.5	- 16m	- 0.6
◐₉	Moor End Farm, Broxted	N51 54.6 E000 17.9	- 16m	- 0.8
◐₁₀	Goodacres, Broxted	N51 55.1 E000 17.4	9m	+ 0.2
◐₁₁	Chickney Hall Villas, Broxted	N51 55.5 E000 17.3	-15m	-1.3

If the aircraft was required to take-off with a tailwind an amount of the noise recorded at the noise monitor should be disregarded.

Tailwind component	≤1 KT	≤2 KT	≤3 KT	≤4 KT	>4 KT
Amount to be disregarded	0.4 dB	0.8 dB	1.2 dB	1.6 dB	2.0 dB

CHANGES: SIDs renumbered.

© JEPPESEN, 2003, 2010. ALL RIGHTS RESERVED.

2

Most piston engine aircraft do not have sufficient climb performance to enable them to reduce power after departure, and as most light aircraft operate VFR they will not follow the instrument departure routings. Therefore any noise abatement procedure will only affect the lateral profile flown. The following lists the most common noise complaints associated with the operation of light aircraft:

i.   Circuit training
ii. Parachute dropping/Glider tug towing
iii. General noise pattern of a piston engine aircraft
iv. Aerobatics
v.   Low level flying
vi. Ground running of engines

It is in the interests of all airfield operators to be good neighbours and to integrate the operations of the airfield into the local community. Therefore, most airfields will voluntarily create NAPs and noise limiting procedures to minimise noise levels. All licensed airfield's NAPs will be listed in the appropriate entry in the AIP, and those for non-licensed airfields are listed in a suitable commercial publication such as 'Pooley's Flight Guide'.

■ *Figure 2-3*
An extract from the UK AIP describing Denham's Noise Abatement Procedures (NOT FOR OPERATIONAL USE)

EGLD AD 2.21 NOISE ABATEMENT PROCEDURES

(a) Circuits should be flown as small as practicable without reducing flight safety.

(b) Runway 24 Departures: After take-off continue straight ahead until past the houses on the right, then turn right before the A413 road to avoid overflying Gerrards Cross.

(c) Runway 06 Departures: Turn left over the lakes to avoid Harefield.

(d) Runway 24 Arrivals: From Maple Cross, fly the base leg over the lakes to avoid Harefield.

(e) Runway 06 Arrivals: From Chalfont St Giles, the base leg should be flown to the east of the A413 road to avoid Gerrards Cross.

(f) Circuit Traffic: Circuit traffic should stay south of Hogtrough Wood to avoid a noise sensitive area in Chalfont St Peter. Additional restrictions apply to twin-engined aircraft and helicopters at weekends.

(g) North of the London CTR aircraft should fly as high as permitted. ATSOCAS may be obtained from Northolt Approach on 126.450 MHz.

2

Figure 2-4
An extract from Pooley's
Flight Guide describing
Chichester Goodwood's
Noise Abatement
Procedures (NOT FOR
OPERATIONAL USE)

CHICHESTER (Goodwood)   2013
Noise Abatement Procedures

Fixed Wing:

Standard join is overhead at 2000 ft. 'Straight-in' and 'base' joins are strongly discouraged when circuit is active. Outside ATS hours and after sunset, overhead join is madatory.

Circuit height: 1200 ft QFE. No fixed-wing circuits after 1400 on Sundays.

Circuit directions: Rwys 06,10 and 14L/14R – Left Hand.

Rwys 24, 28 and 32L/32R – Right Hand.

Note: Rwy 14L/32R **in use** 1 Nov to 31 Mar only.

Runway 06
Take-off: No restrictions.
Landing: No low approaches over the built up-areas in the undershoot.

Runway 24
Take-off: As soon as practicable after departure, turn right to avoid built up area. Maintain track until reaching or passing circuit height. No practice engine failures after take-off until west of A286 road.
Landing: No restrictions.

Runway 14L/14R
Take-off: Turn left as soon as practicable after departure to avoid overflying the school and houses under the climb out path. No practice engine failures after take-off until well clear of the school and houses.
Landing: No low approaches over East Lavant village. Light aircraft should aim to touch down beyond the intersection of runways 10 and 14.

Runway 32L/32R
Take-off: Turn right 20° as soon as practicable after departure to avoid East Lavant village. Maintain that heading until well beyond the village. No practice engine failures after take-oft until well beyond the village.
Landing: No restrictions.

Runway 10
Take-off: No restrictions.
Landing: No restrictions.

Runway 28
Take-off: Maintain runway heading until clear of Lavant village.
Landing: No restrictions.

Helicopters:

Circuit height: 900 ft QFE or as directed by ATS.   No helicopter circuits on Sun.
Circuit directions: When Rwys 14 or 32 are in use, circuits are flown from the 'triangle' and are flown inside and below the fixed wing circuit.
When Rwys 06,10, 24 or 28 are in use, circuits are flown from Rwy 32 threshold parallel to, but in opposite direction to the fixed wing circuit, i.e to the south of aerodrome.
Helicopters are to avoid routeing over Chichester, Westerton and Summersdale. Helicopters are not permitted to join the circuit below 700 ft QFE unless weather dictates a lower height.

Noise Abatement and Circuits – see opposite and page 184.

2

■ *Figure 2-5*
An extract from Pooley's
Flight Guide describing
Chichester Goodwood's
Noise Abatement
Procedures (NOT FOR
OPERATIONAL USE)

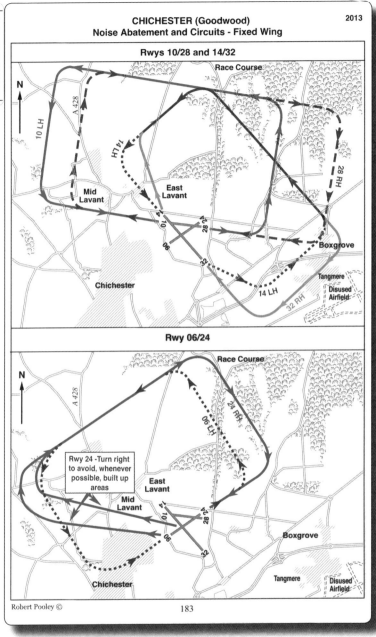

Robert Pooley ©   183

The complexity of the NAP depends on the surrounding neighbourhood, terrain, runway layout, and type of aircraft using the airfield. Noise Preferential Routings are created to stop aircraft flying over certain areas and certain airfields have a variable circuit pattern to avoid aircraft repeatedly flying over the same houses. Examples of simple NAPs are as follows:

i.   After departure avoid flying over the village of Cranfield.
ii.   Pilots should route to the East of Whitstable.
iii. After departure pilots should set course from overhead or abeam Congleton VRP.
iv.   Power checks should be conducted on the Alpha taxiway.
v.   Pilots are encouraged not to complete repetitive Practice Forced Landings over the area surrounding Deal.

Airfields that have very noise sensitive surrounding areas and have different types of aircraft using the airfield may have more complex NAPs. ICAO provides two Noise Abatement Departure Procedures (NADPs) which are designed for large aircraft, however, these do not apply to light aircraft. Examples of more complex NAPs applicable to light aircraft which you may find at smaller airfields are shown below:

i.   All turbojet aircraft shall apply ICAO NADP 1.
ii.   After departure all aircraft must turn at 500ft onto a track of 030° until reaching 1500ft before setting course.
iii. Pilots must leave the VRP of Mars on a track of 140°, upon crossing the railway line fly towards the 'tall tower' and intercept the final approach course.
iv.   All aircraft must follow the M25 motorway and join on an extended final reporting at approximately 4 miles (overhead the 'Golf course') and 2 miles (the 'Tall Tower').
v.   All pilots must obtain a briefing from ATC before departure.

Before visiting an airfield, review the NAPs in the AIP for a licensed airfield and a commercial flight guide in the case of an unlicensed one. After reading the procedures, if you are still in doubt about what to do, contact the airfield and obtain a briefing. The CAA produce a document entitled 'Noise Abatement at GA Aerodromes' which gives a more detailed description about NAPs. One final point:

NOISE ABATEMENT PROCEDURES DO NOT APPLY IN THE EVENT OF AN EMERGENCY.

RUNWAY INCURSION AWARENESS (MEANING OF SURFACE MARKINGS AND SIGNALS)

A runway incursion is defined as the following:

A **Runway Incursion** is any occurrence at an airport involving the unauthorised or unplanned presence of an aircraft, vehicle, or person on the protected area of a surface designated for aircraft take-offs and landings.

They are caused by a variety of reasons but pilot/air traffic controller workload, distraction and incorrect radio phraseology are often cited as primary causes.

Whilst rare, runway infringements can have catastrophic results; below are a selection of accidents caused by an aircraft manoeuvring on a runway without clearance (credit to www.SKYbrary.com):

i.   On 2 July 2008, an Air Tran Airways B737-700 which had just landed at night on runway 34C at Seattle-Tacoma, failed to hold clear of runway 34R during taxi as instructed and passed almost directly underneath a North West Airlines A330-200 which had just become airborne from Runway 32R. The Investigation found that the 737 crew had been unaware of their incursion and that the alert provided by the airport surface detection equipment had not provided an opportunity for ATC usefully to intervene to stop prevent the potential conflict.

ii. On 12 January 2006, an Air China Boeing 747-200, which had just landed at Frankfurt failed correctly to understand and read back its taxi-in clearance and the incorrect read back, was not detected by the controller. The 747 then crossed another runway at night and in normal visibility whilst an A320 was landing on it. The A320 responded by increased braking and there was consequently no actual risk of collision. The controller had not noticed the incursion and, in accordance with instructions, all stop bars were unlit and the RIMCAS had been officially disabled due to too many nuisance activations.

2

iii.   A Boeing 737 (B737), operating a scheduled service from Aberdeen to London Gatwick, at a speed of 100kt was obliged to abort its take-off run to avoid a possible collision with a Super Puma (AS332L) helicopter. The helicopter had been hovering at a holding point close to the upwind end of the runway when, because of the crew's misinterpretation of their clearance, it manoeuvred to hover above the runway into the path of the departing B737.

iv.   On 30 October 2009, a Bombardier DHC8-400 being operated by Flybe on a scheduled passenger flight from Exeter to Edinburgh failed to follow its acknowledged ATC taxi out clearance to the runway holding point 08 and entered and lined up on the active runway at night in normal visibility at the same time as a Boeing 737-500 being operated by Astraeus Airlines on a non revenue positioning flight to Exeter, was landing on the opposite (26) direction of the same runway. The landing B737 was able to stop before reaching the other aircraft and clear the runway.

v.   On 8th October 2001, a Boeing MD-87 being operated by SAS and departing Milan Linate on a scheduled passenger flight to Copenhagen in thick fog in daylight collided at high speed with a German-operated Cessna Citation taxiing for departure on a non scheduled passenger flight from Paris Le Bourget. The MD-87 failed to get airborne and continued along the ground until it impacted, still at high speed, a ground handling building. Both aircraft caught fire and were destroyed. All 114 occupants of both aircraft and 4 personnel on the ground were killed. The Italian ANSV carried out an Investigation. It was found that, unknown to ATC because of the prevailing thick fog, the Cessna had failed to follow the taxi clearance issued and correctly acknowledged and had eventually entered the active runway after crossing a lit red stop bar just as the departing MD-87 was reaching V_R at the same point. The Investigation was unable to find any evidence that either of the Cessna pilots was trained or authorised to operate a public transport flight departure in the prevailing low visibility. The majority of the investigation concentrated on documenting the widespread organisational failings which, although they had not been the direct cause of the accident and its aftermath, it was concluded had facilitated the accident scenario.

Depending on the complexity of the airfield, taxiing can often be one of the hardest parts of operating a light aircraft. If you are learning to fly

at a large international airport such as Newcastle or Edinburgh, you have probably already found that it can be quite confusing which way to go in order to get to, or from, the runway. Not to mention having larger aircraft moving around you!

■ *Figure 2-6*
Having large aircraft moving around you can be daunting!

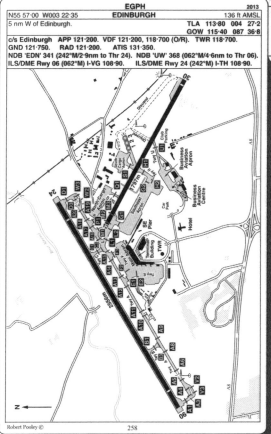

■ *Figure 2-7* Taxiing a light aircraft at a large airport such as Edinburgh isn't easy!

2

Because airport taxiways and runways layouts can be confusing ICAO defines visual aids in order to standardise airport markings around the world. This enables pilots to recognise the difference between runway markings and taxiways whether they are operating at a small grass airport or a large international one. The CAA produce CAP 637 'Visual Aids Handbook' which is a compendium of Visual Aids intended for the guidance of Pilots and Personnel engaged in the handling of aircraft.

Aerodrome Signals & Markings (Rules 56–60)

A signals area is positioned near the control tower at some aerodromes to allow messages to be passed to a pilot without the use of radio:

- **in flight,** by signals laid out on the ground; and
- **on the ground,** by signals hoisted up a mast located in the signals area.

SIGNALS AND MARKINGS IN THE SIGNALS AREA

Direction of Take-Off and Landing

A **white 'T'** signifies that aeroplanes and gliders taking off or landing shall do so parallel with the shaft of the 'T' and towards the cross arm, unless otherwise authorised by the appropriate ATC unit.

A **white disc** at the head of the 'T' means that the direction of landing and the direction of take-off do not necessarily coincide. This latter situation may also be indicated by a **black ball** suspended from a mast. A rectangular **green flag** flown from a mast indicates that a right-hand circuit is in force.

■ *Figure 2-8* **Direction of take-off and landing**

2

Use Hard Surfaces Only

A **white dumb-bell** signifies that movements of aeroplanes and gliders on the ground shall be confined to paved, metalled or similar hard surfaces. The addition of black strips in each circular portion of the dumb-bell, at right angles to the shaft, signifies that aeroplanes and gliders taking off or landing must do so on a runway, but that movement on the ground is not confined to hard surfaces.

■ *Figure 2-9* Use of hard surfaces signals

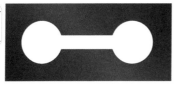 

■ *Figure 2-10* Right-hand circuit indicator

Right-Hand Circuit

A red-and-yellow striped arrow bent through 90 degrees around the edge of the signals area and pointing in a clock- wise direction means that a right-hand circuit is in force.

Where the circuit direction at an aerodrome is variable (left- hand or right-hand) a rectangular **red flag** on the signals mast indicates that a **left-hand** circuit is in operation. A rectangular **green flag** signifies that the circuit is **right-hand.**

■ *Figure 2-11* Special precautions signal

Special Precautions

A red square panel with a single yellow diagonal stripe means that the state of the manoeuvring area is poor and that pilots must exercise special care when landing.

■ *Figure 2-12* Landing prohibited signal

Landing Prohibited

A red square panel with a diagonal yellow cross signifies that the aerodrome is unsafe for the movement of aircraft and that landing is prohibited.

2

Helicopter Operations

A **white 'H'** in the signals area means that helicopters must take off and land only within a designated area (that area itself being marked by a much larger white 'H').

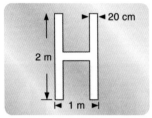

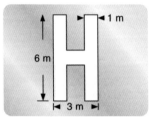

(a) A white letter H is displayed in the signals area

(b) A white letter H indicates the area to be used only by helicopters for take-off and landing

Gliding

A double white cross and/or two red balls suspended from a mast, one above the other, signify that glider-flying is taking place at the aerodrome. (A similar but much larger signal is used to mark an area on the aerodrome which is to be used only by gliders).

A **yellow cross** indicates the tow-rope dropping area.

Tow-ropes, banners, etc. can only be picked up or dropped at an aerodrome, and then only as directed by the aerodrome authority, or in the designated area (yellow cross) with the aircraft flying in the direction appropriate for landing (ANO Article 126 and Rule of the Air 44).

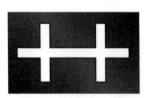

■ *Figure 2-14*
Gliding in progress

SIGNALS ON PAVED RUNWAYS AND TAXIWAYS

Unserviceable Portion of Runway or Taxiway

Two or more white crosses along a section of runway or taxiway, with the arms of the crosses at an angle of 45 degrees to the centreline of the runway or taxiway at intervals of not more than 300 metres, signify that the section of the runway or taxiway marked by them is unfit for the movement of aircraft.

■ *Figure 2-16*
Boundary of
unserviceable
area marker

Orange and white markers as illustrated, spaced not more than 15 metres apart, signify the boundary of that part of a paved runway, taxiway or apron which is unfit for the movement of aircraft. Each marker comprises a base board supporting a slatted vertical board, both of which are striped orange–white–orange.

Holding Point on Paved Taxiway

Parallel yellow lines – usually marked as a set of double continuous and double broken lines – across a taxiway signify a holding point, beyond which no part of an aircraft or vehicle may proceed in the direction of the runway, without ATC permission.

Of the two sets of lines, the **broken yellow lines** are located on the runway side, enabling the pilot to determine if the holding point affects him. Moving in the reverse direction towards a holding point, with the broken yellow lines encountered first (for example, having turned off the runway after landing), the holding point does not require a clearance to cross it.

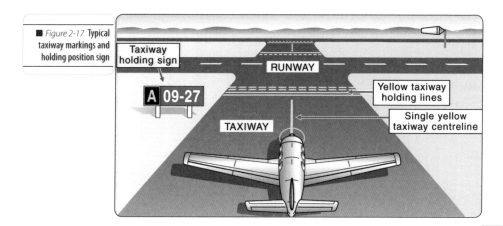

■ *Figure 2-17* **Typical taxiway markings and holding position sign**

Taxiway holding sign

A 09-27

RUNWAY

TAXIWAY

Yellow taxiway holding lines

Single yellow taxiway centreline

2

Note. – Older holding points may be marked with white lines, but most are now yellow. Also, older holding points may still be marked with a single continuous line and a single broken line.

MARKERS ON UNPAVED MANOEUVRING AREAS

Aerodrome Boundary Markers

Orange/white striped wedge-shaped markers (like elongated wheel-chocks in shape), placed not more than 45 metres apart, indicate the boundary of an aerodrome. These are supplemented by flat orange/white markers, also placed 45 metres apart, on any structures which lie on the boundary.

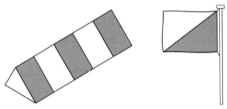

■ *Figure 2-18*
Boundary marker

Unserviceable Portion

The orange/white striped wedge-shaped markers shown above are also used to mark the boundary of an unpaved area which is unserviceable for aircraft movement. These alternate with square flags showing equal orange and white triangular areas. Within this marked area the bad ground is itself marked with one or more white crosses (as described above).

Runway/Stopway Boundary Markers

White, flat rectangular markers, flush with the surface and placed not more than 90 metres apart, indicate the boundary of an unpaved runway or of a stopway. (A stopway is a prepared rectangular area of ground at the end of a runway, in the direction of take-off, designated as a suitable area in which an aircraft can be stopped in the case of an interrupted take-off.)

Light Aircraft Area

A white letter 'L' indicates a part of the manoeuvring area to be used only for the taking off and landing of light aircraft.

Figure 2-19
Light aircraft areas

If a dumb-bell displayed in the aerodrome signals area has a red 'L' superimposed, it means that light aircraft are allowed to take off and land either on a runway or on the area designated by the white 'L'.

Figure 2-20
Runway to be used

Runway to be Used

A white 'T' (placed on the left side of a runway when viewed from the landing direction) indicates that it is the runway to be used. Where there is no runway it indicates the direction for take-off and landing.

Figure 2-21
Landing dangerous

Landing Dangerous

A white cross displayed at each end of a runway indicates that landing is dangerous and that the aerodrome is used for storage purposes only.

Emergency Use Only

Figure 2-22
Emergency use only

A white cross and a single white bar displayed at each end of the runway at a disused aerodrome indicates that the runway is fit for emergency use only. Runways so marked are not safe-guarded and may be temporarily obstructed.

Land in Emergency Only

Figure 2-23
Land in emergency only

Two vertical yellow bars on a red square on the signals area indicate that the landing areas are serviceable but the normal safety facilities are not available. Aircraft should land in emergency only.

DISPLACED THRESHOLD MARKINGS

The threshold marking on a runway delineates the beginning of the usable portion of that runway (at the downwind end). Sometimes the threshold marking is moved, or displaced, some distance up the runway from the end of the paved area. Such a displaced threshold may be either temporary, to allow for maintenance, for instance, or permanent.

There are various displaced threshold markings, depending on the type (if any) of aircraft movement permitted in the first portion of the runway, and whether the displacement is temporary or permanent. Some pre-threshold areas may be usable for take-off, but not for landing; some may be unfit for any kind of aircraft movement.

■ *Figure 2-24* **Normal 'piano key' threshold marking for a paved runway** '09' is the runway designator – the runway direction rounded off to the nearest 10°, 090° in this case

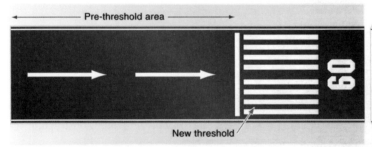

Pre-threshold area

New threshold

■ *Figure 2-25* **Permanently displaced threshold** White arrows indicate that the pre-threshold area is available for taxi and take-off, but not for landing

White crosses, not more than 300 metres apart, arms at 45° to runway centreline

■ *Figure 2-26* **Permanently displaced threshold** White crosses indicate that the pre-threshold area is unfit for movement of aircraft and unsuitable as a stopway

■ *Figure 2-27*
Temporarily displaced threshold
Pre-threshold area is available for taxi and take-off, but not for landing

■ *Figure 2-28*
Temporarily displaced threshold
Pre-threshold area is unfit for movement of aircraft and unsuitable as a stopway

NORMAL THRESHOLD MARKING (TOP) AND DISPLACED THRESHOLD MARKINGS

SUMMARY OF AERODROME SIGNALS VISIBLE ONLY WHEN ON THE GROUND

In the Signals Area

1. A black ball on a mast signifies that the directions of take-off and landing are not necessarily the same.

2. Two red balls on a mast signify that gliding is taking place.

3. A rectangular red/yellow chequered flag or board means that aircraft may move on the manoeuvring area and apron only with the permission of ATC.

■ *Figure 2-29*
ATC in operation

4. If the circuit direction at the aerodrome is variable, and a left-hand circuit is in operation, a red flag will be flown from the mast. A green flag on the mast signifies that a right-hand circuit is in force at the aerodrome. (Note that the colours of the flags for left and right circuits are the same as for aircraft navigation lights.)

Away from the Signals Area

5. A square yellow board bearing a black 'C' indicates the position at which a pilot can report to ATC or other aerodrome authority.

■ *Figure 2-30* **Location of aerodrome authority**

■ *Figure 2-31* Signals area at Wycombe (WP); clockwise from bottom left corner – special precautions; gliding in progress; (white dash symbol is part of dumb-bell not in use); right-hand circuits; and in centre: take-off and landing direction (towards the cross-arm)

2

Light Signals (Rule 61)

You should be aware of standard light signals that ATSU personnel may beam to aircraft. The light signals differ in meaning according to whether you are in flight or on the ground. Green flashes, for instance, when beamed at an aircraft in flight mean "Return for a landing", whereas when beamed to an aircraft on the ground they mean "Authorised to taxi".

FROM ATSU TO AIRCRAFT

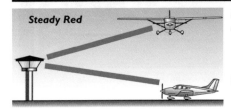

Steady Red

Do not land. Give way to other aircraft and continue circling.

Stop.

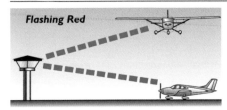

Flashing Red

Do not land. Aerodrome closed (go to another aerodrome).

Move clear of landing area.

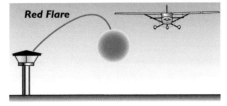

Red Flare

Do not land; wait for permission.

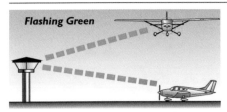

Flashing Green

Return to this aerodrome and wait for permission to land.

Cleared to taxi on the manoeuvring area if pilot satisfied no collision risk exists.

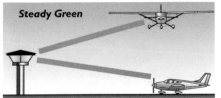

Steady Green

Cleared to land if pilot satisfied no collision risk exists.

Cleared to take-off if pilot satisfied no collision risk exists.

FROM ATSU TO AIRCRAFT

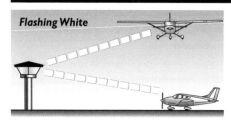

Flashing White

Land at this aerodrome after receiving a steady green light

Return to starting point on aerodrome.

Light signals can also be sent from an aircraft, but the equipment (such as flares) is rarely available for a pilot to use. The one signal that can be used in almost any aircraft, however, is flashing the landing lights or position navigation lights on and off (usually visible from the ground only at night) to indicate "I am compelled to land".

FROM AIRCRAFT TO ATSU

Flashing landing and/or navigation lights

I am compelled to land.

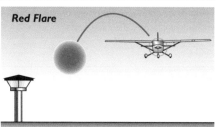

Red Flare

Immediate assistance required.

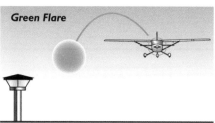

Green Flare

By night
May I land?

By day
May I land in a different direction from that indicated by the landing T?

FROM MARSHALLER TO PILOT (RULE 62)

Proceed under guidance of another marshaller

Right or left arm down, the other arm moved across body and extended to indicate position of the other marshaller.

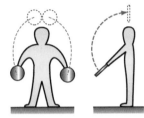

Move ahead

Arms repeatedly moved upward and backward, beckoning onward.

Open up starboard engine(s) or turn to port

Right arm down, left arm repeatedly moved upward and backward. The speed of arm movement indicates the rate of turn.

Open up port engine(s) or turn to starboard

Left arm down, the right arm repeatedly moved upward and backward. The speed of arm movement indicates the rate of turn.

Stop

Arms repeatedly crossed above the head. The speed of arm movement indicates the urgency of the stop.

2

FROM MARSHALLER TO PILOT (RULE 62)

Start engine

A circular motion of the right hand at head level, with the left arm pointing to the appropriate engine.

Chocks inserted

Arms extended, the palms facing inwards, then swung from the extended position inwards.

Chocks away

Arms down, the palms facing outwards, then swung outwards.

Cut engines

Either arm and hand placed level with the chest, then moved laterally with the palm facing downwards.

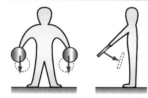

Slow down

Arms placed down, with the palms towards the ground, then moved up and down several times.

Slow down engine(s) on indicated side

Arms placed down, with the palms towards the ground, then either the right or left arm moved up and down indicating that the motors on the left or right side, as the case may be, should be slowed down.

FROM MARSHALLER TO PILOT (RULE 62)

This bay

Arms placed above the head in a vertical position.

Release brakes

Raise arm, with fist clenched, horizontally in front of the body, then extend fingers.

Engage brakes

Raise arm and hand, with fingers extended, horizontally in front of body, then clench fist.

All clear – marshalling finished

The right arm raised at the elbow with the palm facing forwards.

Start engine(s)

Left hand overhead with the number of fingers extended, to indicate the number of the engine to be started, and circular motion of right hand at head level.

Back aircraft tail to starboard

Point left arm down, move right arm down from overhead, vertical position to horizontal forward position, repeating right arm movement.

FROM MARSHALLER TO PILOT (RULE 62)

Back aircraft tail to port

Point right arm down, move left arm down from overhead, vertical position to horizontal forward position, repeating left arm movement.

 indicates that the signal is applicable only to helicopter operations.

 Hover

Arms placed horizontally sideways.

 Land

Arms placed down and crossed in front of the body.

Move upwards

Arms placed horizontally sideways with the palms up beckoning upwards. The speed of the arm movement indicates the rate of ascent.

Move downwards

Arms placed horizontally sideways with the palms down beckoning downwards. The speed of arm movement indicates the rate of descent.

Move horizontally

Appropriate arm placed horizontally sideways, then the other arm moved in front of the body to that side, in the direction of the movement, indicating that the helicopter should move horizontally to the left or right side, as the case may be, repeated several times.

2

FROM MARSHALLER TO PILOT (RULE 62)

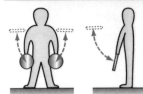

 Move back

Arms placed down, the palms facing forward, then repeatedly swept up and down to shoulder level.

 **Release load**

Left arm extended horizontally forward, then right arm making a horizontal slicing movement below left arm.

FROM PILOT TO MARSHALLER (RULE 63)

Brakes engaged

Raise arm and hand with fingers extended horizontally in front of face, then clench fist:

Brakes released

Raise arm with fist clenched horizontally in front of face, then extend fingers:

Insert chocks

Arms extended palms facing outwards, move hands inwards to cross in front of face:

Remove chocks

Hands crossed in front of face, palms facing outwards, move arms outwards:

FROM PILOT TO MARSHALLER (RULE 63)

Ready to start engines

Raise the number of fingers on one hand indicating the number of the engine to be started. For this purpose the aircraft engines shall be numbered in relation to the marshaller facing the aircraft, from his right to his left.
For example, No. 1 engine shall be the port outer engine, No. 2 shall be the port inner, No. 3 shall be the starboard inner, and No. 4 shall be the starboard outer.

In order to highlight where a runway incursion risk is more likely **'runway incursion hotspots'** are marked on airport taxiway charts. A **'runway hotspot'** is an area, which has the potential of being, or has had a higher number of runway incursions due to the complexity of the taxiways, number of runways, traffic flow, etc. At the planning stage, it is good airmanship to review these areas, and the route you may take to get to the departure runway. If you are flying with another pilot, ask them to monitor the taxi routing to ensure you are adhering to your ATC clearance.

■ *Figure 2-32* Hot Spots–see example of an extract from the Pooleys UK Flight Guide, Aberdeen EGPD, highlighting this hotspot.

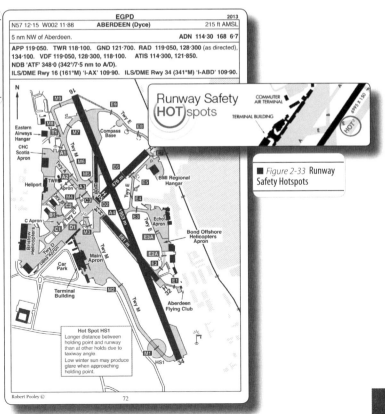

■ *Figure 2-33* Runway Safety Hotspots

2

Airports have a variety of methods to warn the pilot that they are approaching a runway holding point, the position of which ensures that a safe clearance exists between the aircraft holding and any aircraft passing in front of it. The diagram below is an extract from CAP 637 showing taxiway markings:

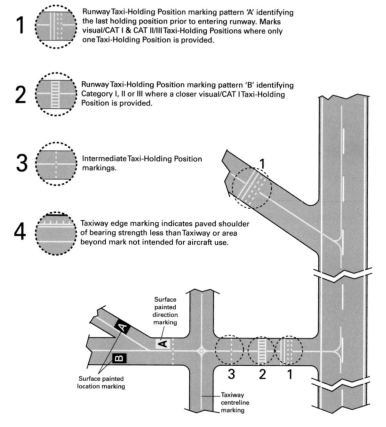

1   Runway Taxi-Holding Position marking pattern 'A' identifying the last holding position prior to entering runway. Marks visual/CAT I & CAT II/III Taxi-Holding Positions where only one Taxi-Holding Position is provided.

2   Runway Taxi-Holding Position marking pattern 'B' identifying Category I, II or III where a closer visual/CAT I Taxi-Holding Position is provided.

3   Intermediate Taxi-Holding Position markings.

4   Taxiway edge marking indicates paved shoulder of bearing strength less than Taxiway or area beyond mark not intended for aircraft use.

The last holding position marking is an important sign to remember (item 1 in the CAP 637 extract). You must not cross this without a specific clearance to do so, however, when vacating the runway after landing, you do not need to gain permission to cross it.

■ *Figure 2-34* Runway holding point – do not cross without a clearance

■ *Figure 2-35*
A runway holding point as seen when vacating a runway - a clearance is not required: remain on the tower frequency until instructed to change

To provide a further warning of the close proximity of a runway guard lights may be fitted. These are one pair of alternating flashing yellow lights, situated on either side of the runway, (wider taxiways may have them stretched over the full width) often referred to as 'Wig Wags'.

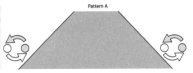

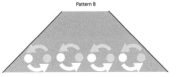

■ *Figure 2-36*
Runway wigwags are fitted to provide a warning

■ *Figure 2-37*
Runway guard lights (picture A) and 'Wig Wag lights (picture B)

2

Airfields certified for Low Visibility Procedures (LVPs) will have red Stop Bars at certain holding points. Stop Bars consist of a group of red lights situated at 90° to the taxiway and face the oncoming traffic. Put simply, they act like traffic lights, therefore you must **NOT** cross a lit stop bar. When ATC issues a line-up or take-off clearance they switch off the Stop Bars. They are on a timing circuit so if you delay lining up they may come on again before you have passed them.

■ *Figure 2-38*
Never Cross
-illuminated Stop Bars

Of course a smaller grass strip also presents its challenges with regard to runway infringement, as it can sometimes be difficult to distinguish the taxiway from the runway. All licensed airfields, however, will have signage delineating the runway.

Opposite is an extract from CAP 637 showing taxiway holding positions.

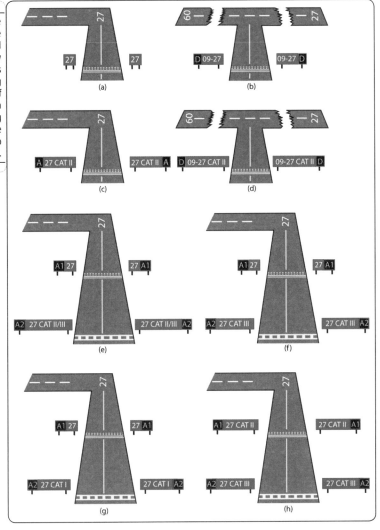

■ *Figure 2-39* **These diagrams illustrate typical signs associated with various Runway Taxi-holding positions on Taxiway 'A' leading to the threshold of Runway 27 and on Taxiway 'D' leading to an intermediate taxiway entrance to Runway 09-27.**

Note. – *The signs at intermediate taxiway entrances as shown at (b) and (d) show the runway designation in both directions; a left turn is required to reach the threshold of Runway 09 and a right turn to reach the threshold of Runway 27.*

CAT I, II and III relate to a category of Instrument Landing System which aircraft use in bad weather; the worse the weather, the more the radio signal has to be protected, hence why the holding points move further away from the runway.

2

The marker boards used at smaller airfields are often portable and these can be blown over by the preceding aircraft, or the board itself might be obscured by grass. Runway markings are sometimes not as easy to see from the ground as they are from the air. Non-radio

■ *Figure 2-40*
Runway holding position sign at the take-off end of Runway 14 with co-located Taxiway Alpha location sign.

aircraft may also operate from the airfield increasing the likelihood of a runway incursion if a light signal was misunderstood.

The airport operator has an obligation to maintain the signage and runway markings, but do not be afraid to inform the operator either over the radio or in person about any signs/markings which may need attention.

■ *Figure 2-41*
Well-kept runway markings on a grass runway

The taxi-out, take-off, approach, landing, and taxi-in phases of the flight are all safety critical; therefore it is prudent to adopt a 'sterile cockpit' policy. A sterile cockpit is one where only tasks relating to the handling and safety of the aircraft for the related phase of flight are carried out. European rules governing commercial operators state the following with regard to sterile cockpit:

EU-OPS.1085 Rule 9 States:

The commander shall not permit any crew member to perform any activity during take-off, initial climb, final approach, and landing except those duties required for the safe operation of the aeroplane.

Whilst this rule is clearly aimed at commercial operators operating in a multi-pilot environment, when you obtain your PPL(A) you will undoubtedly take friends and relatives flying who will be sitting next to you. They will most likely be unfamiliar with the aviation environment and will naturally be inquisitive. It is good airmanship to explain to passengers that taxi, take-off, approach, landing and taxi-in are critical phases of flight, therefore it is best to ask questions once you are in the cruise. However, all passengers no matter where they are sitting, should be encouraged to mention anything that concerns them.

An essential part of taxiing safely and in accordance with the clearance (and flying in general) is Situational Awareness (SA). SA is about knowing where you are in relation to what is going on around you. SA is fluid, therefore it needs to be updated constantly, it is best described by the following cycle:

When applied to taxiing an aircraft, SA is about constantly asking yourself, 'Where am I in relation to my clearance limit, where is the runway and where are the other aircraft moving around me going?'

To help you answer these questions here are some tips:

- Have a taxi chart to hand and mark the clearance limit.
- Know where you are going **BEFORE** you start taxiing.
- Keep your eyes outside the cockpit.
- Listen to what ATC have told you to do-if in doubt stop.
- Don't rush.
- Taxi at an appropriate speed - CAA guidance is to taxi defensively
- Make sure you have selected the correct radio frequency and have the next frequency in standby.
- Make sure the volume level is correctly set.
- Keep on the yellow centreline.

- If you are following an aircraft don't get too close to it.
- Anticipate the next turn and taxiway.
- Listen to ATC transmissions and build up a mental picture of where people are going, what's moving around you and how they may affect you.

Situational Awareness relies on having spare mental capacity. In the early stages of training you are unlikely to have much of this, because you will be still learning how to taxi the aircraft and understand what is being said on the radio. However, as you progress through the course taxiing will become second nature, and you will be able to analyse what is going on around you.

Some light aircraft fitted with advanced avionics have the ability to display a taxi chart with the aircraft's current position superimposed on the display. This enables the pilot to update their Situational Awareness and confirm that the correct routing is being followed. It also allows the pilot to concentrate on taxiing the aircraft whilst not having to look inside the cockpit to find paper charts at a critical time. However, as with any cockpit instrumentation avoid being 'heads in' for a protected period of time.

■ Figure 2-42
The Avidyne Ex600 Multi Function Display has the ability to display the aircraft's current position on the taxi chart.

To increase SA and consequently reduce the risk of making a mistake whilst taxiing, consider adopting the following best practices (your instructor may well have additional advice):

- Review the airport diagram and check any NOTAMs that may affect a taxi route.
- Brief passengers regarding a sterile cockpit – but not to keep quiet if they see something that concerns them!
- Familiarise yourself with all possible taxi routes.
- Listen to the ATIS before taxiing to establish the runway in use.
- At smaller airfields look at the windsock or direction of departing/ landing aircraft to establish the runway in use.
- Have a taxi chart to hand.
- Monitor the taxi route on the moving map.
- Write down the clearance limit and identify it on the taxi chart.
- Put the transponder to ground mode to enable ATC to monitor your position.
- **NEVER** cross-illuminated red Stop Bars.
- Avoid completing checks whilst approaching and/or crossing runways.
- If in doubt, **STOP** and ask ATC for clarification, or help if needed.

The use of correct radio phraseology is an important part of avoiding runway incursions. CAP 413 Radiotelephony Manual and Air Pilot's Manual Volume 7 describe all aviation phraseology in detail. The following text regarding clearances is applicable at controlled airports. For communications at non-controlled airports refer to CAP 413 or APM 7.

Callsigns for Aircraft

PILOT: Oxford Tower, G-ABCD, request Basic Service.

ATC: G-ABCD, Oxford Tower, pass your message.

After satisfactory communication has been established and provided that no confusion is likely to occur, the ground station may abbreviate callsigns (see table below). A pilot may only abbreviate the callsign of his aircraft if the aeronautical station has first abbreviated it. For example:

FULL CALLSIGN	ABBREVIATION
GABCD	G-CD
Jetset GABCD	Jetset CD
N31029	N029
Thomson 12A*	No abbreviation
Cessna GABCD **	Cessna G-CD
Helicopter GABCD **	Helicopter G-CD

* Represents a Type C callsign.

** The name of either the aircraft manufacturer, or name of aircraft model, or name of the aircraft category (e.g. helicopter or gyrocopter) may be used as a prefix to the callsign.

Taxi Clearances

Taxi instructions issued by a controller will always contain a clearance limit, which is the point at which the aircraft must stop, unless further permission to proceed is given. For departing aircraft, the clearance limit will normally be the holding point of the runway in use, but it may be any other position on the aerodrome depending on the prevailing traffic. Pilots should, wherever possible, note taxi clearances down. For example:

PILOT: Shoreham Tower, G-ABCD, DA-40 by the south side hangars request taxi for VFR flight to Calais, 2 POB.

ATC: G-ABCD, squawk 3763 taxi holding point K1 runway 20 via taxiway Kilo, QNH 967 hectopascals.

2

If the instructions given to surface traffic involve crossing a runway in use, clearance to cross should normally be withheld until no confliction exists. However, to achieve greater efficiency of operation, clearance to cross may be given subject to aircraft which are landing or taking off. The conditional clearance shall contain sufficient information to enable the pilot of the taxiing aircraft or vehicle driver to identify the other traffic and should be related to one movement only. For example:

ATC: JETSET 007, after the landing A320, via Bravo 1 cross runway 26, report vacated.

PILOT: After the landing A320, via Bravo 1 cross runway 26, wilco, JETSET 007.

■ *Figure 2-43*
Always write down the taxi clearance limit

Conditional clearances, in which an ATC issues an instruction that becomes valid after another event has occurred, have been identified as a contributory factor in a significant number of incidents, particularly in relation to clearances issued to aircraft in the vicinity of a runway.

Conditional clearances are only to be provided subject to conditions specified by the relevant authority. Conditional phrases will not be used for movements affecting the active runway(s), except when the aircraft or vehicles concerned are seen by the controller and pilot. Conditional clearances are to relate to one movement only and, in the case of landing traffic; this must be the first aircraft on approach. A conditional instruction shall be given as follows:

1.   Call sign;
2.   The condition;
3.   Identification of subject of the condition;
4.   The instruction.

2

FOR EXAMPLE:

ATC: JETSET 007, after the landing PA-28, line up.

PILOT: After the landing PA-28 line up, JETSET 007.

Take-off Clearance

Except in cases of emergency, messages will not be transmitted to an aircraft in the process of taking off or in the final stages of an approach and landing. Controllers will use the following phraseology for take-off.

ATC: G-CD, cleared for take-off

PILOT: Cleared for take-off, G-CD

BEFORE LINING UP SUMMARY:
- Look left and right and check the approaches and runway are clear.
- Position the aircraft at 90° to the runway to ensure maximum field of vision.
- Turn aircraft lights on.
- Identify the correct runway.
- Check that runway Stop Bars have been extinguished.
- Avoid completing non-essential tasks whilst lining up.
- Ensure transponder is selected on.
- Do not stop on a runway unless told to do so, or if it's an emergency.
- Do not enter without a specific clearance from ATC.
- Use correct radio phraseology.

FURTHER READING
The following documents give more guidance on avoiding runway incursions and you may find them useful in preparing for your exam:

- UK AIC P 52/2005.
- FAA RUNWAY INCURSION AVOIDANCE.
- CAP 413.
- CAP 637 VISUAL AIDS HANDBOOK.

NOW COMPLETE – CHAPTER 2 QUESTIONS

2

Chapter 3

FIRE OR SMOKE

Cause

All fires must have 3 components to sustain combustion, as shown in the triangle below:

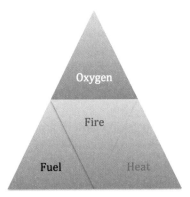

If any one component is removed from the triangle then the fire will extinguish. The types of components found in aircraft are as follows:

Oxygen = Atmosphere, portable breathing equipment for high altitude flight, oxygen generators used in pressurised cabins, chemical reactions between components.

Fuel = Fuel, hydraulic fluid, oil, or any combustible material.

Ignition = Engine ignition system, hot pipes, internal combustion chamber, cigarettes, electrical system, lightning strikes, static charges, arcing.

A fire in an aircraft is a rare event and it is most likely to occur due to poor maintenance, failing components, or incorrect adherence to manufacturers' procedures. Although rare, a fire in any aircraft is about the most serious situation a pilot can face. Actions must be immediate, accurate and effective. **DO NOT DELAY**: investigations have revealed that an aircraft's structural integrity is affected within minutes of a major fire taking hold. There are four causes of fire in an aircraft:

1. Engine start.
2. Inflight.
3. Electrical.
4. Post-crash.

In all cases, the pilot must fly the aircraft first, get the aircraft on the ground as quickly as possible, declare a '**MAYDAY**' and action the appropriate checklist or drill. Any drill, procedure or checklist associated with fire or smoke should be memorised. Commercial operators call these checks 'Memory Items'. The objective of an engine fire or smoke checklist is threefold:

1. Extinguish the fire &/or smoke.
2. Get the aircraft on the ground as quickly as possible.
3. Minimise damage to other critical components.

Smoke is just as much of a threat if not a greater one, due to physiological effects that smoke inhalation and impaired vision have on the pilot and his ability to fly the aircraft.

WARNING:
The following text is general in nature and in all cases the instructions in appropriate AFM/POH/Checklist must be followed.

Carburettor Fire

Over priming the engine can cause excess fuel to enter the air intake; if the engine backfires during start the excess fuel may ignite. This can be quite difficult to detect because the fire may be contained within the carburettor; or the fire may have extinguished itself before detection. It's only when maintenance is being carried out that evidence of a fire is noticed.

The first actions after suspecting, or detecting a carburettor fire, are to continue turning the engine over and draw excess fuel back into the induction system. If the fire is present before the engine has started running, or the fire persists for more than a few seconds, then the engine must be shutdown and aircraft evacuated.

Generic actions for a carburettor fire are as follows:

1. Starter... Crank engine
2. Mixture... Idle Cut-Off
3. Throttle.. Open
4. Electric fuel pump (if fitted).................... Off
5. Fuel selector..................................... Off

Subsequent actions:

6. Ignition... Off
7. ATC (if able)...................................... Inform
8. Electric Master................................... Off
9. Locate fire extinguisher and evacuate upwind of the aircraft.

3

Engine Fire

An engine fire in flight is often preceded by another indication other than visible flames around the coaming. A fuel check, or pressure drop, may indicate a leak, which may cause a fire; a rough running may indicate a damaged cylinder causing fuel or oil to spill into the engine component.

Any one of the following may also be evidence of an engine fire:

1.   Flames &/or smoke around the engine.
2.   Increased cabin temperature especially in the foot-well.
3.   Fuel smell.
4.   Rough running or engine failure.
5.   Fire warning system (if fitted).
6.   ATC may try to contact you.
7.   Other aircraft.
8.   Passengers.

The colours of the flames indicate the fuel source of the fire. Black coloured flames indicate oil based and orange fuel based.

■ *Figure 3-1*
Oil based fire

Once you have confirmed the engine fire, your actions need to be carried out immediately.

Generic actions for an engine fire are as follows:

1. Fuel Selector......................................Off
2. Throttle...Closed
3. Mixture..ICO
4. Electric fuel pump (if fitted).....................Off
5. Heater...Off
6. Defroster..Off
7. Execute power-off landing

Once the checklist has been completed in a single engine aircraft you have no choice but to execute a forced landing. This may also be appropriate in a multi-engine aircraft if the fire is not extinguished. The type of descent flown is dependent on whether fire or smoke is still present. If either fire or smoke still exists then an emergency descent might be the appropriate course of action. Be aware that fire can damage the aircraft's wing spar very quickly. The wing spar carries the major structural load in an aircraft, so descending rapidly may exert extra strain on the aircraft. Of course there is a balance between getting the aircraft on the ground ASAP,

3

and the potential of structural damage; this is a decision that can only be made on the day.

There are two accepted techniques of emergency descent, unless prohibited by the aircraft manufacturer:

1. Initially roll 30° AOB to maintain a positive load factor, lower the nose and once established in the descent return to wings level. Descend at a high speed-not above VNE; or
2. Reduce speed to below VFE and VLE and lower the flaps and landing gear (if applicable) then descend at the most limiting manoeuvre speed.

In both cases, at a suitable altitude, execute the applicable emergency descent profile and adjust speed for a forced landing in a suitable field.

Technique 1 requires a high-speed descent: as such, consideration to V_A must be given in turbulent air. In an aircraft fitted with a variable pitch propeller, positioning the RPM lever to 'high' will allow the aircraft to act as an aerodynamic brake and prevent excessive airspeed building up. If a fire still exists after the checklist is completed, the high airflow generated by the high speed may extinguish the fire during the descent.

Technique 2 increases the drag on the aircraft by extending the flap and landing gear and thus increasing the rate of descent. The applicable flap and landing gear extension speed limitations must be observed in the descent. This imposes less strain on the airframe and puts the aircraft in a configuration for landing sooner.

Transmit a '**MAYDAY**' call to ATC as high as possible, as the radio range increases with altitude. Whichever technique is used, check every 500-1000ft during the descent, to assess whether the fire still exists and manoeuvre the aircraft over a suitable landing area.

Before practising this manoeuvre during training, you MUST conduct an excellent lookout in the airspace immediately below the aircraft and it is good airmanship to inform ATC.

3

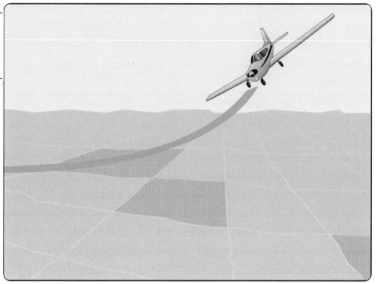

■ *Figure 3-3*
Emergency
descent-check every
500-1000ft whether
the fire still exists

Fire in the Cabin and Cockpit (choice of extinguishing agents according to fire classification and use of the extinguisher)

A fire in the cabin may occur due to any one of the following reasons:

1. Faulty wiring in the avionic components.
2. Smoking.
3. Cigarette lighter igniting a material.
4. Flammable cargo.
5. Fuel line puncture.
6. Thermal runaway in a battery in a personal tablet/laptop.

The most common cause is an electrical fire caused through arcing within the wiring circuitry or a faulty avionic component. Electrical fires are identified by an acrid smell and fine, light grey/white smoke coming from the instrument panel. If the faulty component is easily identified, then the first course of action is to turn it off and locate the fire extinguisher. If you have a passenger, then it may be appropriate for them to fight the fire whilst you fly the aircraft and action the checklist. Always follow the actions described in the aircraft AFM/POH as procedures differ greatly

3

between aircraft. Generic actions for an electrical fire are as follows:

1. Battery master.................................... Off
2. Cabin vents....................................... Open
3. Cabin heat .... OFF
4. Locate BCF fire extinguisher
5. Land as soon as practicable

In a piston-engine aircraft using AVGAS, turning off the Alternator and Battery Master switch will not cause the engine to stop, however, in diesel engine aircraft it might do depending on whether the ECU has a standby power source. Therefore be prepared to execute a forced landing without power. Cabin vents are opened to increase ventilation and aid smoke removal. Before turning off the battery or avionics master switch (if fitted) remember to declare a 'MAYDAY', and consider lowering flap and/or landing gear if they require electric power.

Fires are classified into four types:

Class A – Solids.
Class B – Flammable liquids.
Class C – Electrical.
Class D – Metals.

FIRE CLASS	MATERIAL	EXTINGUISHING AGENT	AGGRAVATED BY	SMOKE COLOUR & CHARACTERISTICS
A	Wood, paper, cloth or plastic	Requires a cooling agent, e.g. water, tea, coffee, etc. Water or Glycol is the best	Alcohol	Grey/brown Thick depending on quantity of fuel source
B	Flammable liquid, hydraulic fluid, oil, tar, or aircraft fuel	Foam or Halon, fire extinguisher	Water will not extinguish the fire	Black Very thick, with a distinct oil/petrol-like odour
C	Electrical	Non-conducting mixture, in order to avoid electrocution and damage to electrical circuitry, e.g. Halon fire extinguisher	Water	Light grey or white, with a bluish tinge. Very fine and can disperse rapidly. Has a distinct acrid odour.
D	Metals, such as sodium, magnesium, lithium, and potassium	Special powder extinguishers are effective on class D fires, because of the possible chemical reaction between the burning and extinguishing agents	Halon fire extinguishers	-

Class A and C fires are the most common in aircraft cabins. Larger aircraft may have multiple types of portable fire extinguisher on board, however, on a light aircraft only one is fitted which must be within easy access for the pilot whilst in the seat position.

Halogenated hydrocarbons (Halons) have been practically the only fire-extinguishing agents used in civil aviation. Unfortunately, Halon is damaging to the environment and aids global warming, and its production has been banned by international agreement. However, because of its special properties and aviation's unique operational environment an exemption has been given for its use, although production of new extinguishers has been extremely limited. Halon is the generic name for the group of BromoChlorodiFluoromethane (BCF) extinguishers that can be used for class A, B, and C fires making them ideal for use in all aircraft. However, do not use Halons on a class D fire. Halon agents may react vigorously with the burning metal. For information only-other extinguishing agents used in aviation have the following properties:

1. CO_2, which smothers the fire out, as it is heavier than Oxygen and forces itself immediately around the material. The problem with using this in a confined space is that it can cause unconsciousness, and death by suffocation, if the victim is allowed to breathe CO_2 in fire extinguishing concentrations for 20 to 30 minutes. It is not effective as an extinguishing agent on fires involving chemicals containing their own oxygen supply, such as cellulose nitrate (used in some aircraft paints) and fires involving magnesium and titanium.

2. Dry chemical extinguishing agents can be used on Class A, B, and C fires. Dry chemical powder extinguishers contain mono- ammonium phosphate. All other dry chemical powders are restricted to Class B or C fires. Dry powder chemical extinguishers create a lot of residue, which is not ideal in the confines of an aircraft cockpit or cabin!

3. Water can be used on Class A type fires by cooling the material below its ignition temperature and soaking the material to prevent re-ignition. Water is not suitable for Class C fires, so generally water-based extinguishers are not used on board an aircraft.

The following hand-held extinguishers are unsuitable as cabin or cockpit equipment:

- CO_2.
- Dry chemicals (due to the potential for corrosion damage to electronic equipment, potential for obscuring instrumentation, and the clean up problems from their use).
- Specialised dry powder (suitable for ground operations).

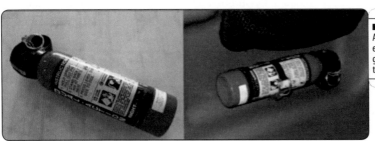

■ *Figure 3-4*
A portable fire extinguisher-Halon gas is the most popular type in light aircraft.

Hand-held fire extinguishers discharge an extinguishing agent for 8 to 25 seconds, depending on their type and capacity. It is therefore essential that you select, and know how to use the fire extinguisher properly. It is good airmanship also to brief passengers on how to use the fire extinguisher. Using the mnemonic PASS can help when remembering how to use a fire extinguisher:

PULL the pin;
AIM the fire extinguisher at the base of the fire;
SQUEEZE the top handle or lever;
SWEEP the fire extinguisher nozzle from side to side in a sweeping motion.

WARNING: *Because of the chemical composition of HALON it is three times as effective as CO_2 extinguishers that contain the same amount of extinguishing agent. Airline crews are advised to use Portable Breathing Equipment (PBE) if using it in a confined space. Therefore it is advisable to increase ventilation in the cockpit and wear an O_2 mask if one is on board. If used on Class A fires the surrounding area should be cooled with a non-alcoholic liquid.*

FURTHER READING
The following articles are excellent and provide further reading if required:

- FAA ADVISORY CIRCULAR 120-80.
- AIRBUS FLIGHT OPERATIONS BRIEFING NOTES, CABIN OPERATIONS, MANAGING IN-FLIGHT FIRES.
- FAA AIRPLANE FLIGHT MANUAL, CHAPTER 17, FIRE PROTECTION SYSTEMS.

Smoke in the Cockpit and Cabin
(Effects and action to be taken)

The first priority when dealing with a fire is to extinguish it, the second is to remove the smoke/fumes created by burning material. Smoke inhalation is often the primary cause of death in a household fire and the same is true in an aircraft one, large or small.

The gases contained within the smoke depend on the material being burnt. Aircraft are constructed of the following combustible materials:

- Synthetic Material.
- Wood.
- Petro Chemicals.
- Metal.
- Natural Cloths.
- Plastic.
- Wiring.

The two main toxic gases contained within smoke are:

- Carbon Monoxide.
- Hydrogen Cyanide.

Most materials contain Carbon; consequently they release both Carbon Monoxide and Dioxide when burnt. You may have seen a Carbon Monoxide detector fitted in the cockpit; this is because broken cabin heaters can leak Carbon Monoxide from engine exhaust gases into the cabin. Carbon Monoxide is an odourless, and colourless gas, so a detector which changes colour when it comes into contact with it is fitted to warn the pilot of its presence.

Carbon Monoxide affects people in different ways and the levels required to induce derogation in a pilot's performance vary greatly. The following are possible symptoms and effects of Carbon Monoxide poisoning:

Spot The Danger

HOME & TRAVEL
VISUAL AWARENESS CO DETECTOR

DATE OPENED

DARK SPOT INDICATES DANGER

ECO-FRIENDLY
NO BATTERIES OR POWER SOURCE REQUIRED
INSTALL IN SECONDS

■ *Figure 3-5*
A typical CO detector for a light aircraft

3

- Headache.
- Weakness.
- Nausea.
- Dizziness.
- Confusion.
- Dimness of Vision.
- Impaired Judgement.
- Unconsciousness leading to Death.

Synthetic materials found in the cabin will contain Hydrogen which, when burnt, produces Hydrogen Cyanide gas which is highly toxic. Symptoms of Hydrogen Cyanide poisoning are similar to those of Carbon Monoxide with the addition of possible convulsions and vomiting. The effects of Hydrogen Cyanide poisoning are rapid.

Smoke has numerous further effects on the occupants:

- Reduces Visibility.
- Disorientation.
- Eyes, Nose and Throat Irritation.
- Hypoxia.
- Increased Breathing Rate.

Because of the speed at which the smoke and fumes can reduce pilot performance, the removal checklist MUST be carried out without delay. Generic actions to be followed in the event of smoke in the cabin are as follows:

1.   Source of fire .... Check

Electrical fire (smoke in cabin):

2.   Master switch..................................... OFF
3.   Vents.. OPEN
4.   Cabin heat... OFF
5.   Locate fire extinguisher
6.   Land as soon as practicable

3

If the smoke is still not clearing, consider cracking open one of the doors or ventilation windows. Transmit a '**MAYDAY**' call to ATC before turning off the master switch, because the radio will be turned off, as a consequence of actioning the smoke checklist.

Pressurised aircraft will be fitted with Oxygen masks for the pilots, which have the facility to provide 100% Oxygen delivered under a positive pressure, allowing the pilots to breathe uncontaminated air. Unfortunately, most light aircraft do not have them fitted, however, covering the nose and mouth with a damp cloth will provide protection from smoke particulates and will absorb most of the water-soluble gases (i.e. hydrogen cyanide and hydrogen chloride). This gives the pilot valuable time to get the aircraft on the ground, and provides (albeit limited) protection from the effects of smoke inhalation.

■ *Figure 3-6*
If you have an oxygen mask fit it when dealing with a smoke or fumes incident

FURTHER READING
The following article is excellent and provides further reading if required:

* MEDICAL FACTS FOR PILOTS - SMOKE TOXICITY. PUBLICATION AM−400−95/1 WRITTEN BY: ARVIND K. CHATURVEDI, PH.D. PREPARED BY: FAA CIVIL AEROSPACE MEDICAL INSTITUTE AEROSPACE MEDICAL EDUCATION DIVISION.

NOW COMPLETE – CHAPTER 3 QUESTIONS

3

Chapter 4

WINDSHEAR AND MICROBURST

Effects and Recognition during Departure and Approach

The Effect of Windshear

Windshear is defined as a change in wind direction and/or speed in space. The term 'Windshear' simply describes a changing wind. This can result in a wind the speed of which alters as an aircraft climbs or descends or the direction of which changes from place to place. It can generate a downdraft through which an aircraft has to fly. Windshear is generally understood to mean a wind change within a short distance or a short time.

OVERSHOOT EFFECT. Flying into an updraft will increase the rate of climb and will increase the angle of climb relative to the ground. Flying into a downdraft will have the opposite effect.

Because of its own inertia (or resistance to change), an aeroplane flying into an increasing headwind will want to maintain its original speed relative to the ground. Thus the effect of flying into an increasing headwind will be to increase the airspeed temporarily.

Attempting to maintain the correct climbing speed by raising the nose will lead to increased climb performance (only transient as the shear is flown through).

In this way, the climb performance will increase when flying into an increasing headwind, a decreasing tailwind or into an updraft. The aeroplane has a tendency to overshoot, or go above, the original flightpath, or to gain airspeed temporarily – hence the term overshoot effect.

4

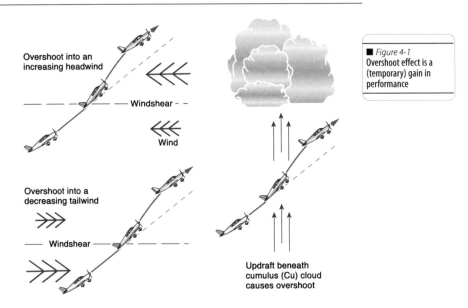

Overshoot into an increasing headwind

Windshear

Wind

Overshoot into a decreasing tailwind

Windshear

Updraft beneath cumulus (Cu) cloud causes overshoot

■ *Figure 4-1*
Overshoot effect is a (temporary) gain in performance

Again, the advantages of taking off into wind are clear. Wind strength usually increases as you climb away from the ground, so you would normally expect an aircraft taking off into the wind to climb into an increasing headwind. This leads to increased climb performance over the ground, i.e. a steeper climb-out gradient over ground obstacles.

UNDERSHOOT EFFECT. Taking off downwind, the aeroplane would normally climb into an area of increasing tailwind. Due to its inertia, the aeroplane would temporarily tend to maintain its original speed over the ground, leading to a decreased airspeed. To maintain the target climb speed, the pilot would have to lower the nose. Climb performance, both rate and gradient, would fall off.

Exactly the same effect of decreased climb performance will occur flying into an increasing tailwind, a decreasing headwind, or a downdraft. The aeroplane will tend to fall below the original flightpath, or to lose speed, hence the term undershoot effect.

An initial overshoot effect (for example, when flying into an increasing headwind coming out of the base of a cumulonimbus storm cloud) may be followed by a severe undershoot effect as you fly into the downdraft and then the rapidly increasing tailwind. Treat cumulonimbus clouds with great caution.

Avoid flying near cumulo-nimbus (Cb) clouds.

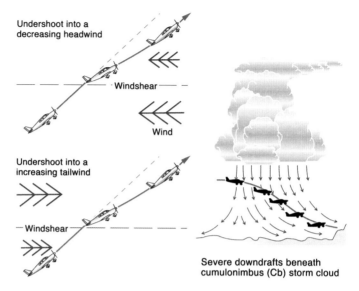

Undershoot into a
decreasing headwind

Windshear

Wind

Undershoot into a
increasing tailwind

Windshear

Severe downdrafts beneath
cumulonimbus (Cb) storm cloud

Windshear

The study of windshear and its effect on aeroplanes and what protective measures can be taken to avoid unpleasant results is still in its infancy and much remains to be learned. What is certain is that every aeroplane and every pilot will be affected by windshear – usually the light windshears that occur in everyday flying, but occasionally a moderate windshear that requires positive action from the pilot and, on rare occasions, severe windshear that can put an aeroplane out of control.

Severe windshears have caused the loss of a number of aircraft, some of them large passenger aircraft. A little knowledge will help you understand how to handle windshear and how to avoid unnecessary problems with it.

4

WINDSHEAR TERMINOLOGY

A windshear is defined as a change in wind direction and/or wind speed, including updrafts and downdrafts, in space. Any change in the wind velocity (be it a change in speed or in direction) as you move from one point to another is a windshear. The stronger the change and the shorter the distance within which it occurs, the stronger the windshear.

Updrafts and downdrafts are vertical components of wind. The most hazardous updrafts and downdrafts are usually those associated with thunderstorms.

The term low-level windshear is used to specify the windshear, if any, along the final approach path prior to landing, along the runway and along the take-off/initial climb-out flightpath. Windshear near the ground (i.e. below about 3,000 ft) is often the most critical in terms of safety for the aeroplane.

Turbulence is eddy motions in the atmosphere which vary with time and from place to place.

EFFECTS OF WINDSHEAR ON AIRCRAFT

Most of our studies have considered an aeroplane flying in a reasonably stable air mass which has a steady motion relative to the ground, i.e. in a steady wind situation. We have seen how an aeroplane climbing out in a steady headwind will have a better climb gradient over the ground compared to the tailwind situation, and how an aeroplane will glide further over the ground downwind compared to into wind.

In reality an air mass does not move in a totally steady manner – there will be gusts and updrafts and changes of wind speed and direction which the aeroplane will encounter as it flies through the air mass. In this chapter, we look at the transient effects that these windshears have on the flightpath of an aeroplane.

A Typical Windshear Situation

Often when the wind is relatively calm on the ground, at several hundred feet above the ground the light and variable wind conditions change suddenly into a strong and steady wind. If we consider an aeroplane making an approach to land in these conditions, we can see the effect the windshear has as the aeroplane passes through the shear.

4

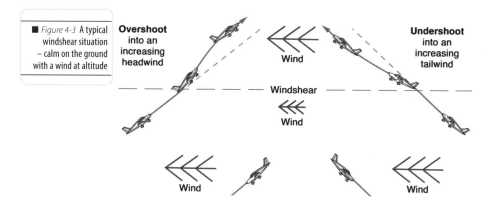

■ *Figure 4-3* A typical windshear situation – calm on the ground with a wind at altitude

An aeroplane flying through the air will have a certain inertia depending on its mass and its velocity relative to the ground. If the aeroplane has a true airspeed of 80 knots and the headwind component is 30 knots, then the inertial speed of the aeroplane over the ground is (80 – 30) = 50 knots.

When the aeroplane flies down into the calm air, the headwind component reduces quickly to say 5 knots. The inertial speed of the aeroplane over the ground is still 50 knots, but the new headwind of only 5 knots will mean that its true airspeed has suddenly reduced to 55 knots.

In gusty conditions, use a power-on approach and landing, and consider adding a few knots to the approach speed.

The pilot would observe a sudden reduction in indicated airspeed and a change in the performance of the aeroplane – at 55 knots airspeed the performance will be quite different from when it is at 80 knots airspeed. The normal reaction would be to add power or to lower the nose to regain airspeed, and to avoid undershooting the desired flightpath.

The pilot can accelerate the aeroplane and return it to the desired flightpath by changes in attitude and power. The more the windshear, the more these changes in power and attitude will be required. Any fluctuations in wind will require adjustments by the pilot, which is why you have to work so hard sometimes, especially when approaching to land.

Overshoot and Undershoot Effect

The effects of windshear on an aeroplane's flightpath depend on the nature and location of the shear, as follows.

4

OVERSHOOT EFFECT

Overshoot effect is caused by a windshear which results in the aeroplane flying above the desired flightpath and/or an increase in indicated airspeed. The nose of the aircraft may also tend to rise. Overshoot effect may result from flying into an increasing headwind, a decreasing tailwind, from a tailwind into a headwind, or an updraft.

UNDERSHOOT EFFECT

Undershoot effect is caused by a windshear which results in an aircraft flying below the desired flightpath and/or a decrease in indicated airspeed. The nose of the aircraft may also tend to pitchdown. Undershoot effect may result from flying into a decreasing headwind, an increasing tailwind, from a headwind into a tailwind, or into a downdraft.

Note that the actual windshear effect depends on:

1.   The nature of the windshear.
2.   Whether the aeroplane is climbing or descending through that particular windshear.
3.   The direction in which the aeroplane is flying.

WINDSHEAR REVERSAL EFFECT

Windshear reversal effect is caused by a windshear which results in the initial effect on the aeroplane being reversed as the aircraft proceeds further along the flightpath. It would be described as overshoot effect followed by undershoot, or undershoot followed by overshoot effect, as appropriate.

Windshear reversal effect is a common phenomenon often experienced on approach to land, when things are usually happening too fast to analyse exactly what is taking place in terms of wind. The pilot can, of course, observe undershoot and overshoot effect and react accordingly with changes in attitude and/or thrust.

4

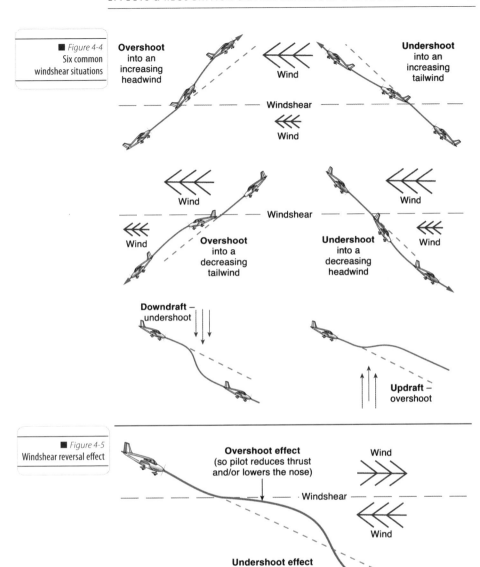

■ *Figure 4-4*
Six common windshear situations

Overshoot into an increasing headwind

Wind

Undershoot into an increasing tailwind

Windshear

Wind

Wind

Windshear

Wind

Wind

Overshoot into a decreasing tailwind

Undershoot into a decreasing headwind

Wind

Downdraft – undershoot

Updraft – overshoot

■ *Figure 4-5*
Windshear reversal effect

Overshoot effect (so pilot reduces thrust and/or lowers the nose)

Wind

Windshear

Wind

Undershoot effect (pilot now needs to add thrust and/or raise the nose)

4

CROSSWIND EFFECT

Crosswind effect is caused by a windshear which requires a rapid change of aircraft heading to maintain a desired track (not uncommon in a crosswind approach and landing because the crosswind component changes as the ground is neared).

■ *Figure 4-6*
Crosswind Effect

THE CAUSES OF WINDSHEAR

Causes of windshear include the wind being slowed down by ground surface roughness, abrupt changes in terrain, thunderstorms, cumulonimbus clouds, large cumulus clouds (downbursts and gust fronts), low-level jetstreams, fronts, thermal activity, sea breezes, etc.

Avoid thunderstorms and cumulonimbus clouds as windshear effects near them can be severe. A strong downburst out of the base of one of these clouds will spread out as it nears the ground. The initial effect may be an overshoot effect followed by what may be an extremely severe undershoot.

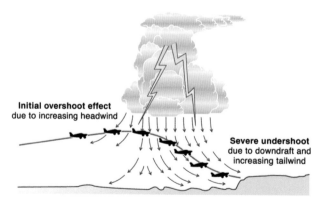

Initial overshoot effect
due to increasing headwind

Severe undershoot
due to downdraft and
increasing tailwind

■ *Figure 4-7*
Avoid thunderstorms
and cumulonimbus
clouds

ACTIONS TO AVOID AND ACTIONS TAKEN DURING ENCOUNTER

At the planning stage, study Significant Weather Charts and Terminal Aerodrome Forecasts for the likelihood of thunderstorms and strong gusty winds. The relevant airfield entry in the AIP might indicate that the airfield is prone to low-level windshear when the wind favours a specific direction. In flight listen to the airfield ATIS (if it has one) and contact the ATSU early for the local weather conditions/pilot reports. If you have the ability to obtain satellite weather reports, then do so for your destination and alternate airfield(s).

If it seems likely that you may encounter windshear ensure, that you carry extra fuel for both holding and diversion. The best action to avoid a windshear or microburst encounter is delay the take-off/landing, or if airborne, to divert to another airfield. However, if you inadvertently experience windshear or a microburst then CAA AIC 84/2008 gives the following guidance:

- Recognise and execute the escape manoeuvre in the AFM.
- Adopt an appropriate pitch angle and try and hold it; do not 'chase' airspeed.
- Be guided by stall warnings when holding or increasing pitch, easing the back pressure as required to attain or hold a lower pitch attitude if necessary. (In many aircraft types optimum performance is very close to the point of onset of stall warning. It is important, however, not to go beyond the point of onset as it is then not possible for the pilot to know how deeply into the warning the aircraft is).

Please note that the techniques described above are aimed at commercial aircraft, which have more power available to escape the windshear or microburst.

Following recovery from a windshear encounter, report it to ATC as reports of windshear encounters are important sources of information to warn other pilots of the danger. The UK AIP (GEN 3-5-21) contains guidance on windshear reporting. AIC 84/2008 concludes with the following:

Recognise – that windshear is a hazard and the signs that may indicate its presence;
Avoid – windshear by delay or diversion;
Prepare – for an inadvertent encounter by a 'speed margin' if 'energy loss' is expected;
Recover – know the techniques recommended for your aircraft and use them without hesitation if windshear is encountered;
Report – immediately to ATC controlling the airfield at which the incident

occurred and using the Mandatory Occurrence Reporting Scheme, to the Civil Aviation Authority.

Even if windshear has not been reported and there is no weather associated with it in the vicinity, always check the wind before commencing the take-off or landing; either by obtaining the ATIS, or asking for a 'wind check' from the ATSU. Certain localised wind directions may create low-level wind shears close to the ground.

The runway in use will normally be that most closely aligned to the surface  wind direction but may vary because of local operational restrictions or procedures. If you are unable to accept the runway in use you should advise ATC, the FISO, or Air/Ground communication service radio station operator, that the crosswind (or tailwind) on that runway is outside your limits and request the use of a more suitable runway. There might be a delay in ATC complying with your request, and in certain cases diversion to an alternate aerodrome with a more suitable runway direction might be the only option.

If you are unable to accept the runway in use inform ATC

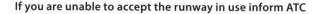

FURTHER READING:
The following articles may prove useful when preparing for your exam:

- AIC P 84/2008.
- AIC P 062/2012

NOW COMPLETE – CHAPTER 4 QUESTIONS

Chapter 5

WAKE TURBULENCE

Cause

As a wing produces lift, the higher static pressure area beneath it forces an airflow around the wingtip into the lower pressure area above. The greater the pressure differential, the greater is this flow around the wingtips.

At the high angles of attack necessary to produce the required lift force at low speeds, very large and strong trailing vortices are formed. As the aeroplane is moving forward, a trail of wingtip vortices is left behind. This effect was discussed under *Induced Drag* – the drag generated by the production of lift.

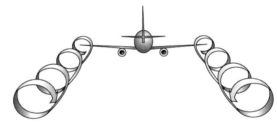

■ *Figure 5-1*
Wake Turbulence

Wake turbulence will be strongest behind a heavy aircraft flying with its flaps up

As a large and heavy aircraft is rotated for take-off or flared for landing, the angle of attack is large. The trailing wingtip vortices formed can be strong enough to upset a following aeroplane if it flies into them. They are invisible but real. This effect is known as wake turbulence.

The main danger from wake turbulence is loss of control caused by induced roll

The wake turbulence behind a *Boeing 747* can significantly affect, for example, a *737* or a *DC-9*, and can cause lighter aircraft to become uncontrollable.

To avoid wake turbulence accidents and incidents, Air Traffic Control delays the operation of light aircraft on runways behind heavy jets for up to 3 minutes before take-off (or 8 nm if landing) to allow the vortices to drift away and dissipate.

All pilots must be aware of wake turbulence because even the Air Traffic Control procedures occasionally provide insufficient separation from the wingtip vortices behind another aircraft. Air Traffic Controllers are experts at their job – do not expect them to be experts at yours as well. As pilot you have the ultimate responsibility for the safety of your aeroplane – so learn to visualise the formation and movement of invisible wingtip vortices.

Heavy aircraft will also leave vortices in their wake in flight, especially in the circuit area where they are flying slowly at high angles of attack – make sure that you provide your own separation in the circuit.

The vortices will tend to lose height slowly (drift downwards) and drift downwind. To be able to avoid these invisible danger areas when following heavier aircraft, you must be able to visualise the movement of the vortices and take steps to avoid them.

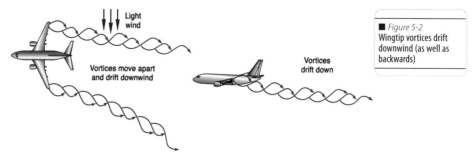

Light wind

Vortices move apart and drift downwind

Vortices drift down

■ *Figure 5-2*
Wingtip vortices drift downwind (as well as backwards)

- A crosswind will cause the vortices to drift off the downwind side of the runway.
- A headwind or a tailwind will carry them down the runway in the direction of the wind.
- In nil-wind or light and variable conditions, the vortices will 'hang around'. Calm conditions can be very dangerous – delaying your take-off or changing runway is worth considering.

Be extra careful in calm conditions, as the vortices will not be blown away.

List of Relevant Parameters

Wake Vortex categories depend on aircraft weight as shown in the table below:

WAKE TURBULENCE CATEGORIES

Category	ICAO and Flight Plan (Kg)	UK (Kg)
Heavy (H)	136,000	136,0000
Medium (M)	< 136,000 and > 7000	< 136,000 and > 40,000
Small (S)	-	40,000 or less and >17,000
Light (L)	7000 or less	17,000 or less

In the UK pilots shall adhere to the UK minimum distance and time separation requirements published in AIC P072/2010 when taking off or landing whether operating in the UK or not. These criteria are:

WAKE TURBULENCE SEPARATION MINIMA – FINAL APPROACH

Leading Aircraft	Following Aircraft	Minimum Distance (Nm)
A380	Heavy/Medium/Small/Light	6/7/7/8
Heavy	Heavy/Medium/Small/Light	4/5/6/7
Medium	Medium/Small/Light	3/4/6
Small	Medium/Small/Light	3/4

Where the leading medium aircraft is a B757 the minimum distance shall be increased to 4 miles. The minima specified in the above table are to be applied when:

a. An aircraft is operating directly behind another aircraft at the same altitude or less than 1000 ft. below; or

b. An aircraft is crossing behind another aircraft at the same altitude or less than 1000 ft. below; or

c. Both aircraft are using the same runway or parallel runways separated by less than 760 m (2500 ft.).

WAKE TURBULENCE SEPARATION MINIMA – DEPARTURES

LEADING AIRCRAFT	FOLLOWING AIRCRAFT	MINIMUM WAKE TURBULENCE SEPARATION AT THE TIME AIRCRAFT ARE AIRBORNE	
A380	Heavy (including A380)	Departing from the same position or From a parallel runway separated < 760m (2500ft)	2 minutes
	Medium (upper and lower)/Small/Light		3 minutes
Heavy	Medium (upper and lower)/Small/Light		2 minutes
Medium (upper and lower)/Small	Light		2 minutes
A380	Heavy (including A380)	Departing from an intermediate point on the same runway or From an intermediate point of a parallel runway separated < 760m (2500ft)	3 minutes
	Medium (upper and lower) Small/Light		4 minutes
Heavy (full-length take-off)	Medium/Small/Light		3 minutes
Medium/Small	Light		3 minutes

The minima specified above apply when the aircraft are using:

a. The same runway;

b. Parallel runways separated by less than 760 m (2500 ft.);

c. Crossing runways if the projected flight path of the second aircraft will cross the projected flight path of the first aircraft at the same altitude or less than 300 m (1000 ft.) below;

d. Parallel runways separated by 760 m (2500 ft.) or more, if the projected flight path of the second aircraft will cross the projected flight path of the first aircraft at the same altitude or less than 300 m (1000 ft.) below.

5

In the event of Wake Turbulence being encountered, *Report Form SRG 1423* should be submitted to:

Wake Turbulence Analysis Team
NATS Corporate and Technical Centre
4000 Parkway
Whiteley
Hampshire
PO15 7FL

Actions taken when crossing traffic, during take-off and landing.

AVOIDING WAKE TURBULENCE

> Avoid wake turbulence by flying above and upwind of the path of other aircraft.

The main aim of wake turbulence avoidance is to avoid passing through it at all, especially in flight.

On Take-Off

When taking off behind a large aircraft which has itself just taken off, commence your take-off at the end of the runway so that you will become airborne in an area well before the point where the heavy aircraft rotated or to where its vortices may have drifted. If doubtful, delay your take-off.

Do not use an intersection departure (less than the full length of the runway) behind a heavy aircraft, as this may bring your flightpath closer to its wake turbulence.

Manoeuvre to avoid the vortices in flight by climbing steeply (but not too slowly, as speed is a safety factor if you strike wake turbulence) or turning away from where you think the wake turbulence is.

When taking off after a heavy aircraft has landed, plan to become airborne well past the point where it flared and landed.

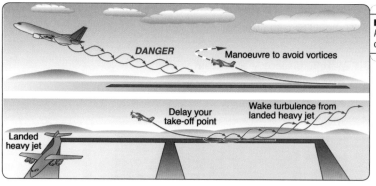

■ *Figure 5-3*
Avoid wake turbulence
on your take-off

If a heavy aircraft has taken off on a different runway and you expect to be airborne prior to the intersection of the runways, observe that the heavy aircraft was still on the ground until well past the intersection, before you commence your take-off.

Always avoid flying through the wake of a heavy aircraft, especially at low speed near the ground.

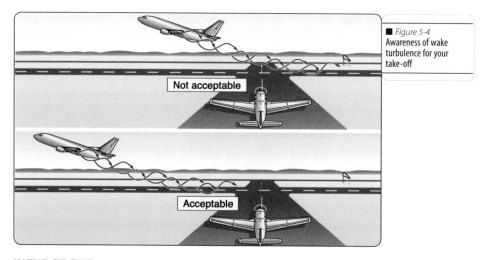

■ *Figure 5-4*
Awareness of wake
turbulence for your
take-off

IN THE CIRCUIT

Avoid flying below and behind large aircraft. Fly a few hundred feet above them, a thousand feet below them or to windward of them. Calm days where there is no turbulence to break up the vortices are perhaps the most dangerous.

5

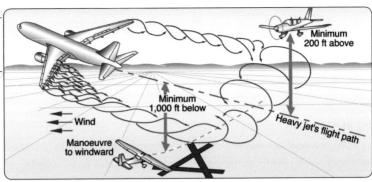

ON APPROACH TO LAND

When following a preceding landing heavy aircraft, fly above its approach path and land well beyond its touchdown point. This is usually possible in a light aircraft landing on a long runway where heavy aircraft are landing.

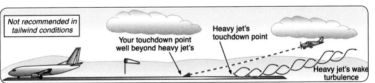

When landing on a runway where a heavy aircraft has just taken off, touchdown well short of its lift-off point or where you think the vortices may have drifted to. The normal touchdown zone will probably ensure this.

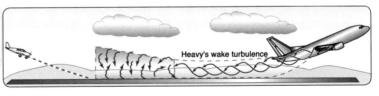

If a preceding heavy aircraft has discontinued its approach and gone around, its turbulent wake will be a hazard to a following aircraft. You should consider changing your flightpath in these circumstances.

5

Note: Accentuated wake
turbulence on Heavy's go-around
HAZARD

■ Figure 5-8
Making an approach
behind a heavy aircraft
that has gone around

JET BLAST

Do not confuse wake turbulence (wingtip vortices) with jet blast (sometimes referred to as thrust stream), which is the high- velocity air exhausted from a jet engine or a large propeller-driven aircraft, especially a turbo-prop. Jet blast can be dangerous to a light aircraft taxiing on the ground behind a jet or large propeller- driven aircraft. Always position your aeroplane when taxiing or when stopped to avoid any potential jet blast.

■ Figure 5-9
Wake turbulence is
different from Jet blast

HELICOPTER ROTOR TIP VORTICES

Helicopters generate significant and powerful rotor tip vortices, particularly when hover-taxiing and hovering, as the rotors are supporting the full weight of the helicopter.

Avoid helicopters
by a wide margin,
especially if they
are hover-taxiing

Take extra care when taking off and landing near air-taxiing helicopters, as their rotor tip vortices will drift downwind, and may drift across your runway. When on final approach, it may not be apparent to you at which stage of flight the helicopter is – so allow a larger space between yourself and the helicopter than you would for an aeroplane of similar size. If in doubt, go around.

More Information

Read the CAA's *General Aviation Safety Sense leaflet No. 15* – it contains excellent practical information on wake turbulence and rotor tip vortices.

Pilots of light aircraft should avoid operating within three rotor diameters of any helicopter in a slow hover taxi or stationary hover. As a visual indicator: if the skids / wheels of the helicopter are resting on the surface then the helicopter will be producing a much reduced downwash. Caution should be exercised however since the helicopter may lift into the hover with little or no notice, thus increasing downwash significantly.

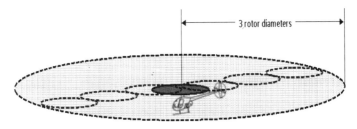

FURTHER READING:

The following material may provide useful when preparing for your exam:

- AIC P072/2010

NOW COMPLETE – CHAPTER 5 QUESTIONS.

5

INTENTIONALLY BLANK

Chapter 6

EMERGENCY & PRECAUTIONARY LANDINGS

Definition

ICAO Annex 12 defines two types of emergencies:

Distress – A condition of being threatened by serious and/or imminent danger and of requiring immediate assistance.

Urgency – A condition concerning the safety of an aircraft or other vehicle, or of some person on board or within sight, but which does not require immediate assistance.

When an aircraft declares an emergency, the state's Rescue Coordination Centre will allocate one of three emergency phases:

Uncertainty Phase: A situation wherein uncertainty exists as to the safety of an aircraft and its occupants.

Alert Phase: A situation wherein apprehension exists as to the safety of an aircraft and its occupants.

Distress Phase: A situation wherein there is a reasonable certainty that an aircraft and its occupants are threatened by grave and imminent danger and require immediate assistance.

■ *Figure 6-1*
Rescue Coordination
Centre

A **Rescue Coordination Centre (RCC)** is a unit responsible for promoting efficient organisation of search and rescue services and for coordinating the conduct of search and rescue operations within a search and rescue region.

When a pilot transmits a distress call on the international distress frequencies of 121.500 or 243 MHz the RCC will be notified and co-ordinate the appropriate response.

Cause

It is impossible to describe every possible scenario which may constitute an emergency and this depends on numerous factors such as type of aircraft, pilot experience, weather conditions, severity of event, time, and system redundancy, etc. Indeed the pilot-in-command can declare an emergency for any condition, which he/she feels puts the aircraft and its occupants in danger. If in doubt, it is wise to ask for help early, before the situation gets critical; you can always downgrade a 'MAYDAY' to a 'PAN' once you have a better grasp of the situation.

As a guide only, the following situations may warrant declaring an emergency using the radio phrase 'MAYDAY, MAYDAY, MAYDAY' in a light aircraft:

- Engine Failure
- Emergency descent
- Fire or Smoke
- Mid-air collision
- Loss of control
- Hijack
- Fuel leak
- Undercarriage failure
- Any time-critical non-normal event

As a guide only, the following situations may warrant declaring an emergency using the radio phrase 'PAN PAN, PAN PAN, PAN PAN' in a light aircraft:

- Alternator failure
- Cracked windscreen
- Landing on a flat tyre
- Sick passenger
- Any non-normal event which is not time-critical

The important thing to do in any non-normal event is to fly the aircraft first, navigate to a point of safety, complete the appropriate checklist, and communicate to both ATC and the passengers. The most common time-critical emergency that affects light aircraft is an engine failure, which can be avoided through proper fuel planning and conducting regular carburettor ice checks. Initial actions following an engine failure/rough running engine are to:

- Trim for the best glide speed (range if overwater)
- Plan forced landing pattern
- Declare a 'MAYDAY' call to ATC and set transponder code 7700
- Complete the following generic fault finding checks:

1. Fuel Selector........................... Tank containing fuel
2. Electric fuel pump.................... ON
3. Mixture................................ Check RICH
4. Carburettor heat .... ON
5. Engine gauges........................ Check for indication of power loss
6. Primer................................. Check locked

If no fuel pressure is indicated, check tank selector position is on a tank containing fuel. Attempt restart, if power is restored:

7. Carburettor heat...................... OFF
8. Electric fuel pump.................... OFF
9. If power is not restored, prepare for a power off landing
  – Trim for best glide speed.

If time permits consider turning the magnetos to 'L' then 'R' then back to '**BOTH**' to isolate a faulty magneto. Move the throttle and mixture controls smoothly to different settings to see if there is a fuel restriction, linkage failure, or too rich/leaner mixture being supplied to the engine. If fuel contamination/starvation is suspected changing tanks will provide an alternate supply.

Note. — that in the case of contaminated fuel, pressure indications will be normal.

6

Once you have transmitted either a '**MAYDAY**' or '**PAN**' call, enter one of following the transponder codes, unless instructed to do otherwise by ATC:

7700 – General Emergency
7600 – Loss of Communication
7500 – Unlawful interference

■ *Figure 6-2*
A radar screen shot of an aircraft squawking 7700

Once the situation has been contained and only if time permits, consider supplying ATC with more information regarding the effect the problem will have on the approach and landing; although more appropriate to larger aircraft, the following mnemonic may help and is often used by commercial pilots (sometimes referred to as a '**NITS**' briefing):

Nature of Problem
Intentions
Time to handle the situation
Special Instructions

FOR EXAMPLE: *Farnborough Radar G-AB, I have suffered an alternator failure, I am diverting to Shoreham airport, I require 5 minutes in my present position to complete the checklist, I will then require a radar heading to Shoreham airport and inform Shoreham ATC that I want to complete a overhead join which may be executed non-radio.*

Passenger Information

The pilot-in-command (PIC) is required by law to complete a safety briefing before departure to all passengers on board the aircraft; however, as the PIC you may have to give them further, more specific instructions in the event of an emergency. There are two categories of emergencies:

1. PLANNED – Time available to brief passengers, secure the cockpit/ seating area, ready emergency equipment.
2. UNPLANNED – No warning given, normally occurs at a critical phase of flight such as the take-off or landing, actions have to be specific and direct.

Items that should be covered during the initial safety brief should include:
- Emergency exit locations and use.
- Operation of seat belts.
- Location and use of both the fire extinguisher and first aid kit.
- Correct seating position and adjustment.
- Instruction to remain clear of the controls.
- Brace position.

The **NITS** briefing described earlier, may serve as a framework to inform the passengers of the situation and what you require them to do. What you tell them, and specifically how to position them for landing will depend on the type of emergency, time available, aircraft type, survival equipment on board, and the landing surface.

In the event of a planned emergency on land instruct passengers:
- To remove all sharp objects, dentures and high-heeled shoes – stow in passenger compartments or under the seat.
- Location of the emergency exit(s) and alternatives.
- How to fasten, tighten seat belts and when and how to release them.
- How to get into the brace position and how long to maintain it for.
- Location and operation of Emergency Locator Transmitter and/or Personal Locator Beacons.

In addition to those points above, in the event of a ditching instruct passengers:

■ *Figure 6-3*
Inflate the life jackets and raft once outside the aircraft

- To don life jackets and inflate them only once outside the aircraft, but before entering the water, or life raft.
- On the location and operation of the life raft, inflate only once outside the aircraft.
- The location of the grab bag (if applicable).

Approximately 15 seconds before impact inform passengers to adopt the Brace position by shouting loudly '**BRACE BRACE, BRACE BRACE, BRACE BRACE**'.

Some modern aircraft such as the Cirrus SR20 and SR22 are fitted with a ballistic parachute recovery system that fires a parachute from the rear fuselage and allows the aircraft to drift down. The operation of this system and different BRACE position should be specifically briefed on the ground, and the PIC should read the applicable entry in the Aircraft Flight Manual regarding its use. Consideration should be given to the type of scenarios it will be deployed.

■ *Figure 6-4*
Cirrus SR20 and SR22 aircraft have a parachute system which requires a specific passenger briefing and brace position.

Evacuation

Touchdown should normally be made at the lowest possible airspeed. When committed to a landing, close the throttle control and turn "OFF" the master and ignition switches. Flaps may be used as desired. Turn the fuel selector valve to "OFF" and move the mixture to idle cut-off. The seat belts and shoulder harness (if installed) should be tightened.

Once the aircraft comes to rest, gather information and assess the situation, if an evacuation is required (following a engine failure for example) complete the evacuation checklist, or equivalent. Once the evacuation checklist is complete, instruct passengers to evacuate the aircraft by shouting '**EVACUATE EVACUATE UNDO YOUR SEAT BELTS AND GET OUT**'. Instruct passengers to use the nearest emergency exit, in the case of a light aircraft with only one door this is pretty obvious however, larger aircraft may have more. Gather any suitable emergency equipment as time permits.

ACTION AFTER LANDING

Post evacuation on land, you should:

- Direct passengers upwind of the aircraft.
- Administer first aid as required.
- Conduct a head count.
- Contact the emergency services.
- Activate Personal Locator Beacons if in a remote location.
- Reassure passengers.
- Do not return to the aircraft unless there is no fire present and it is absolutely necessary for survival.

Post evacuation on water you should:

- Instruct passengers not to inflate their life jackets until outside the aircraft, but before entering the life raft/dinghy or the water if no life raft/dinghy is available.
- Locate the grab bag and life raft – inflate the life raft once outside the aircraft.
- Group passengers together, remain inside the life raft and hold on to any grasp handles fitted.
- Administer first aid as required.
- Activate Personal Locator Beacons.

Ditching in Water

AIM: *To alight on water as successfully as possible, if ditching is the only available option.*

Note. – This exercise is not part of the EASA syllabus.

6

Being forced to ditch in the ocean is a remote possibility; however, it is worthwhile having a suitable procedure in the back of your mind.

Try to land near a ship or in a shipping lane if possible. Make a Mayday radio call before too much height is lost to ensure the best chance of reception by ground stations.

LANDING DIRECTION

If the water is smooth, or smooth with a very long swell, then land into wind.

If there is a large swell or rough sea, then land along the swell, even if you have to accept a crosswind. This avoids the danger of nosing into a big wave. Waves generally move downwind except near a shoreline or in fast-moving estuaries, but swells may not bear any relationship to surface wind direction.

Clues to wind direction include:
- Wave direction;
- Wind lanes (the streaked effect being more apparent when viewed downwind);
- Gust ripples on the water surface;
- Aeroplane drift.

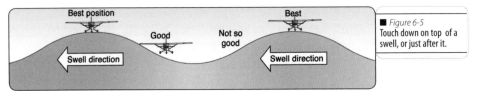

■ *Figure 6-5*
Touch down on top of a swell, or just after it.

FLYING THE MANOEUVRE

If your engine is running, use a powered approach for ditching. From altitude, water generally appears to be calmer than it is. Fly low and study the water surface before ditching.

Generally ditch with an early stage of flap set, using a low speed, a high nose attitude (tail-down) and a low rate of descent controlled by power (if available). Power gives you a lot more control over the touchdown point, so avoid running out of fuel prior to ditching.

Touch down with as low a flying speed as possible, but do not stall in.

ALERT THE PASSENGERS

Warn the passengers. Buckle up and don life-jackets, if available, but do not inflate them until in the water, as they may restrict the evacuation. Remove headsets and anything else that may get in the way during the evacuation.

Be prepared for a double impact – the first when the tail strikes the water, the second (and greater) when the nose hits the water. The aircraft may also slew to one side.

Evacuation (if possible) should be carried out as calmly as possible, life-jackets being inflated outside the cabin. The PIC should supervise.

NOW COMPLETE – CHAPTER 6 QUESTIONS

6

INTENTIONALLY BLANK

6

Chapter 7

CONTAMINATED RUNWAYS

Kinds of Contamination

Take-off and landing performance is affected by, amongst other things, runway surface condition; for example performance calculations on a grass runway will be greater than those on an equivalent tarmac one. A tarmac runway is designed and built to allow precipitation to drain away from the surface, however, when the amount exceeds a natural run off point it will remain on the runway. On a grass runway, or unprepared strip (and to a certain extent a tarmac one too), the drainage depends on local geology, climatology, type of surface, and slope. Matting can be laid on the surface to improve drainage and reduce runway closure periods. When a runway has precipitation on it, it reduces the braking coefficient, which is a measure of the amount of friction available on the runway between the tyre and the surface. The depth and type of precipitation determines the braking coefficient. The more severe the precipitation, the smaller the coefficient and less grip the wheel has on the runway; therefore, the less effective the brakes are at stopping the aircraft.

■ *Figure 7-1*
Take-off and landing performance depends greatly on the runway surface and condition

The following definition of a contaminated runway is the one found in EASA Opinion No 04/2011 Annex 1 (Definitions) and has been adopted by the CAA:

A runway is considered to be contaminated when more than 25% of the runway surface area (whether in isolated areas or not) within the required length and width being used is covered by the following:

a. Surface water more than 3 mm deep, or by slush or loose snow equivalent to more than 3 mm of water;

b. Snow which has been compressed into a solid mass which resists further compression and will hold together or break into lumps if picked up (compacted snow); or

c. Ice, including wet ice.

A typical example of a contaminated runway, that a private pilot may face, is when a small grass airfield's runway becomes FLOODED after a heavy period of prolonged rainfall. It even happens at the larger ones as the picture below shows:

■ *Figure 7-2*
Flooded runway

The presence of water on a runway will be reported to the pilot using the following descriptions:

REPORTING TERM	SURFACE CONDITION
DRY	The surface is not affected by water, slush, snow, or ice. *NOTE: Reports that the runway is dry are not normally passed to pilots. If no runway surface report is passed, the runway can be assumed to be dry.*
DAMP	The surface shows a change of colour due to moisture. *NOTE: If there is sufficient moisture to produce a surface film or the surface appears reflective, the runway will be reported as WET.*
WET	The surface is soaked but no significant patches of standing water are visible. *NOTE: Standing water is considered to exist when water on the runway surface is deeper than 3 mm. Patches of standing water covering more than 25% of the assessed area will be reported as WATER PATCHES and should be considered as CONTAMINATED.*
WATER PATCHES	Significant patches of standing water are visible. *NOTE: Water patches will be reported when more than 25% of the assessed area is covered by water more than 3 mm deep.*
FLOODED	Extensive patches of standing water are visible. *NOTE: Flooded will be reported when more than 50% of the assessed area is covered by water more than 3 mm deep.*

For EU-OPS performance, runways reported as DRY, DAMP or WET should be considered as NOT CONTAMINATED. Runways reported as WATER PATCHES or FLOODED should be considered as CONTAMINATED.

■ *Figure 7-3*
If the runway is anything other than Dry, Damp, or Wet, then the runway will be contaminated.

In the picture above the runway is contaminated with snow; in the UK operators of small airfields (and sometimes large ones too!) do not have the necessary equipment to clear the runway from contaminants and often close the airfield.

Light aircraft are not designed to operate from them so the best advice is to delay take-off or landing, and if necessary, divert to an airfield that has better weather conditions.

ESTIMATED SURFACE FRICTION AND FRICTION COEFFICIENT

Historically runway surface condition reports have been made using any combination of the following methods:

a.   Measuring type and depth of contamination;
b.   Readings from runway friction measuring devices; and
c.   Pilot braking action reports (PIREPs).

There is no universally accepted method to measure the surface friction of a runway and this has led to standardisation issues across the world. The CAA publishes CAP 683 'The Assessment of Runway Surface Friction Characteristics' which describes in great detail the procedures that airfields must adopt when measuring the surface friction of a runway, however, it only applies to paved runways with an Accelerate Stop Distance Available (ASDA) of 1,200 metres or greater in length and used for public transport operations by aeroplanes with a maximum take-off weight (MTOW) in excess of 2730 kg. It is not applicable to grass runways, helicopter landing sites or waterdromes. On paved runways where prescribed public transport operations are not carried out, the application of the procedures is at the discretion of the aerodrome operator.

Therefore, if you operate from an airfield that doesn't meet the criteria above, you have no way of knowing how the brakes will react with precipitation on the runway surface; this is often referred to as the 'braking action'.

For the purpose of a runway surface friction assessment the following definitions apply:

CFME – Continuous Friction Measuring Equipment.

Runway Surface Friction Assessment – The assessment of friction carried out under conditions of self- wetting using a CFME.

Airport operators must periodically assess the runway friction in order to confirm that aircraft will stop safely on a **WET** runway. Runway Surface Friction Assessment only applies to runways that are **NOT** contaminated due to the potential for unreliable readings.

■ *Figure 7-4*
A Continuous Friction
Measuring Unit

A Runway Surface Friction Assessment is achieved by conducting 'Runs' which is where a vehicle drives up and down a runway several times. On each 'Run' the vehicle tows a machine called a Continuous Friction Measuring Unit (CFMU) which has the ability to assess the friction available if the runway were wet. All the results are recorded and then analysed to assess whether any maintenance action is required to improve the surface condition.

In the UK, friction coefficients used to be reported as a two-digit number obtained from measuring friction characteristics on contaminated runways using Continuous Friction Measuring Equipment (CFME). This was stopped a number of years ago and since then UK runway surface condition reports have been given for each third of a runway in the form of type and depth of contaminant together with percentage coverage.

A contaminated runway will have a SNOWTAM issued by the airport operator. A SNOWTAM is a special series NOTAM notifying the presence or removal of hazardous conditions caused by snow, ice, slush, or standing water associated with snow, slush, and ice on the movement area, by means of a specific format.

Essentially, it is informing the pilot of the type of contamination, depth, length of runway available, and braking action (if provided by the airport operator). A SNOWTAM is not easy to decode as you can see from the example below, so reference to the UK AIP, or suitable flight guide, will be required.

GG EGZZSBLL EGZZSLHR
070645 EGLLZGZX
SWEG0149 EGLL 11070620
SNOWTAM 0149
A) EGLL B) 11070620 C) 05 D) . . . P)
C) 09L D) . . . P)
C) 09R D) . . . P)
R) NO S) 11070920 T) DEICING

Where:
A.   AERODROME IDENTIFIER
B.   DATE/TIME OF OBSERVATION (UTC)
C.   RUNWAY DESIGNATOR
D.   CLEARED RUNWAY LENGTH (if less than published length)
E.   CLEARED RUNWAY WIDTH (if less than published width)
F.   DEPOSITS OVER TOTAL RUNWAY LENGTH (Observed on each third of the runway)

G. MEAN DEPTH OF DEPOSITS (mm) (for each third of total runway length)

H. FRICTION MEASUREMENTS OR ESTIMATES (for each third of runway length)

I. Not used

J. CRITICAL SNOWBANKS (if present)

K. RUNWAY LIGHTS (if obscured)

L. FURTHER CLEARING OPERATIONS (if planned)

M. FURTHER CLEARANCE EXPECTED TO BE COMPLETED BY . . . (UTC)

N. TAXIWAY

O. Not used

P. TAXIWAY SNOWBANKS

Q. Not used

R. APRON

S. NEXT PLANNED OBSERVATION/MEASUREMENT

T. PLAIN LANGUAGE REMARKS

Operating on a contaminated runway presents the following problems to **ALL** aircraft:

- Reduced braking action.
- Reduced ground control authority.
- Reduced traffic flow rates.
- Restrictive crosswind limits.
- Reduced operating weights.
- Potential damage to airframe and engines due to ingestion of contaminant.
- Greater potential for runway overrun.

In conclusion, contaminated runway operations in the UK are rare, however, light aircraft are not designed, nor equipped, to operate on contaminated runways, therefore delay departure or arrival, and if airborne divert to the nearest suitable airfield.

7

FURTHER READING:

The following articles and AICs have further guidance and a more in-depth description of operating on contaminated runways, which you may find useful when preparing for your exam:

- CAA INFORMATION NOTICE IN–2013/056
- AIC P 86/2007
- CAP 683

NOW COMPLETE – CHAPTER 7 QUESTIONS.

Questions - Chapter 1

OPERATION OF AIRCRAFT

1. What is definition of a large aeroplane?

    a. An aeroplane of a maximum certificated take-off mass of over 5700 kg.
    b. A jet aeroplane with more than 9 seats.
    c. Any aeroplane with more than 9 seats.
    d. Any aircraft with more than 1 engine.

2. What is the definition of the pilot-in-command?

    a. The pilot who has the most flying experience on board the aircraft
    b. The pilot who sits in the left hand seat.
    c. The pilot designated by the operator or the owner as being in command and charged with the safe conduct of a flight.
    d. The pilot designated by the operator, or the owner as being the person who makes all the critical decisions in flight.

3. What is definition of night?

    a. Any time that Air Traffic Control put the runway lights on.
    b. The hours between the end of evening civil twilight and the beginning of morning civil twilight, or such other period between sunset and sunrise, as may be prescribed by the appropriate authority.
    c. The hours between evening civil twilight and the morning civil twilight or such other period between sunset and sunrise, as may be prescribed by the appropriate authority.
    d. Any time the pilot-in-command cannot see sunlight.

4. What is definition of the Operator?

    a. The person charged by the CAA to operate the aircraft.
    b. The pilot-in-command.
    c. The person or organisation that pays the bills.
    d. A person, organisation, or enterprise engaged in, or offering to engage in, an aircraft operation.

5. What is the definition of Flight Time — aeroplanes?

    a. The total time from the moment an aeroplane first moves for the purpose of taking off until the moment it finally comes to rest at the end of the flight.

    b. The total time from the moment an aeroplane first gets airborne until the moment it finally touches down.

    c. The moment you 'book out' with operations to moment you 'book in'.

    d. The total time the engine is running.

6. What is the ICAO definition of Aerial Work?

    a. Any aircraft operation in which an aircraft is being funded from a commercial venture.

    b. An aircraft operation in which an aircraft is used for specialised services such as agriculture, construction, photography, surveying, observation and patrol, search and rescue, aerial advertisement, etc.

    c. Any aircraft operation in which the pilot-in-command is required to hold a Commercial Pilot's Licence.

    d. An aircraft operation in which an aircraft is used for specialised services such as agriculture, construction, photography, surveying, observation and patrol, search and rescue, private hire and scheduled travel, etc.

7. What is a Flight Manual?

    a. A manual which describes the national aviation authorities' Rules of the Air and associated ICAO differences.

    b. A manual or book which describes how to operate the aircraft.

    c. A manual, associated with the certificate of airworthiness, containing limitations within which the aircraft is to be considered airworthy, and instructions and information necessary to the flight crew members for the safe operation of the aircraft.

    d. A manual containing limitations within which the aircraft is to be considered airworthy, and instructions and information necessary to the flight crew members for the safe operation of the aircraft.

8. What is the definition of a General Aviation Operation?

    a. An aircraft operation other than a commercial air transport operation or an aerial work operation.

    b. An aircraft operation that is general in nature.

    c. An aircraft operation other than a commercial air transport operation or an aerial work operation that uses light aircraft.

    d. An aircraft operation other than a commercial air transport operation or an aerial work operation that uses single engine piston aircraft.

9. What is an Operations Manual?

    a. A manual containing procedures, instructions and guidance for use by operational personnel in the execution of their duties.

    b. A manual or book containing procedures, instructions, and guidance for use by operational personnel in the execution of their duties.

    c. A manual containing procedures, instructions and guidance for use by Operations personnel only.

    d. A manual, associated with the certificate of airworthiness, containing limitations within which the aircraft is to be considered airworthy, and instructions and information necessary to the flight crew members for the safe operation of the aircraft.

10. What is the State of Registry?

    a. The State whose monarchy owns the aircraft.

    b. The State on whose register the aircraft is entered.

    c. The country where the insurance company is registered.

    d. The state where the aircraft is based.

11. What is a Safety Management System?

    a. A systematic approach to managing safety, including the necessary organisational structures, accountabilities, policies, and procedures.

    b. A systematic approach to managing the owners of flying schools, including the necessary organisational structures, accountabilities, policies, and procedures.

    c. A system devised by the Health and Safety Executive to monitor managers of flying schools and other aviation businesses.

    d. A manual containing procedures, instructions and guidance for use by operational personnel in the execution of their duties.

INTENTIONALLY BLANK

Questions – Chapter 2

NOISE ABATEMENT

1. Can the CAA prosecute a pilot for breaking an airfield's Noise Abatement Procedures?

   a. Yes, the CAA can prosecute a pilot for anything they wish.
   b. No, the CAA can only prosecute a pilot for breaking the ANO and Rules of the Air.
   c. It depends on the size and location of the airfield.
   d. The CAA will prosecute a pilot when asked to do so by an airfield operator.

2. Where would you find Noise Abatement Procedures for a licensed airfield?

   a. In the applicable airfield entry in the AIP.
   b. In the ANO.
   c. Each airfield's Noise Abatement Procedures are published in an AIC.
   d. You MUST ring the ATSU for a verbal briefing.

3. Where would you find Noise Abatement Procedures for an unlicensed airfield?

   a. In the applicable airfield entry in the AIP.
   b. In the ANO.
   c. Each airfield's Noise Abatement Procedures are published in an AIC.
   d. In a commercial flight guide such as 'Pooley's Flight Guide'.

4. Should you cross Stop Bars at a runway holding point?

   a. Yes, these are only for large aeroplanes.
   b. Yes, they might be faulty.
   c. No, wait until they have been extinguished by ATC.
   d. Only if you see them.

5. Before entering a runway what should you do regarding lookout?

   a. Look both left and right to check the approach and runway are clear.
   b. Turn off all aircraft lights in order not to dazzle other pilots.
   c. Do nothing; it is ATC responsibility to check that the runway is clear.
   d. Taxi onto the runway very slowly, stop and apply the parking brake, complete the before take-off checklist.

2

6.   Do Noise Abatement Procedures apply to PPL holders?

   a.   No, only to Commercial Pilots
   b.   No, PPL holders generally do not operate at larger airfields, which are the only types
            that have Noise Abatement Procedures.
   c.   No, PPL holders are immune from any penalty that the airfield operator may impose
            on them for disregarding their Noise Abatement Procedures.
   d.   Yes, as most airfields now have Noise Abatement Procedures, PPL holders should
            follow them.

7.   The position of runway holding points ensures:

   a.   That a safe gap exists between the aircraft holding and any aircraft that may pass in
            front of it.
   b.   That a safe gap exists between the aircraft holding and any aircraft that may pass in
            front of, or behind it.
   c.   Nothing is assured-it is the pilot-in-command's responsibility.
   d.   That a safe gap exists to protect the radio signals for the applicable instrument
            approach only.

8.   When lining up on a runway the pilot should:

   1.   Look left and right to check for aircraft or vehicles on the runway.
   2.   Ensure a clearance has been given.
   3.   Put all aircraft lights and transponder on.
   4.   Taxi very slowly onto the runway and always stop and apply the parking brake.

   a.   1,2 & 4.
   b.   All of them.
   c.   1,2 & 3.
   d.   1 & 4.

9.   If in doubt about the correct route to follow whilst taxiing the pilot should:

   a.   Bring the aircraft to a stop, inform ATC, and ask for clarification.
   b.   Bring the aircraft to a stop, shutdown the engine and call ATC using a mobile phone.
   c.   Bring the aircraft to a stop, inform ATC, and call the flying school.
   d.   Keep moving at all times; ATC need to ensure that an efficient flow of traffic exists at
            all times.

10.   What is the correct phraseology for the issue of a take-off clearance?

   a.   ATC: G-CD, cleared for take-off. Pilot: Cleared for take-off, G-CD.
   b.   ATC: G-CD, cleared for departure. Pilot: Cleared for departure, G-CD.
   c.   ATC: G-CD, cleared to go. Pilot: Cleared to go, G-CD.
   d.   ATC: G-CD, cleared to light the fires. Pilot: Cleared to light the fires, G-CD.

11.   Should a clearance limit be written down?

    a.   Yes.

    b.   No.

    c.   Depends on the pilot's mental capacity.

    d.   Only if the pilot is not familiar with the airport.

12.   What is the colour of runway Stop Bars and Guard Lights respectively?

    a.   Red and Yellow.

    b.   Yellow and Blue.

    c.   Blue and Green.

    d.   Red and White.

13.   Regarding taxiing procedures at airports with ATC which of the following statements is correct?

    1.   The position of the runway holding point ensures that a sufficient margin exists between the holding aircraft, and any aircraft passing in front of it.

    2.   You may cross a runway Stop Bar, once a clearance has been received by ATC and they have been extinguished.

    3.   You may cross two solid and two broken yellow lines only after a specific clearance to do so has been given and after you have checked both left and right for traffic.

    4.   You may cross a dashed yellow line only after a specific clearance to do so has been given.

    a.   1, 2, & 3.

    b.   All of them.

    c.   1 & 4 only.

    d.   1, 2, & 4.

2

INTENTIONALLY BLANK

Questions – Chapter 3

FIRE OR SMOKE

1. How many components must a fire have?

    a. 2.
    b. 3.
    c. 4.
    d. 5.

2. What are the four major phases/causes of aircraft fire?

    1. Engine start.
    2. Circuits.
    3. Electrical.
    4. Re-fuelling.
    5. Post-crash.
    6. Inflight.
    7. Passengers smoking.

    a. All of them.
    b. 1, 2, 5, & 6.
    c. 1, 3, 5, & 6.
    d. 2, 3, 5, & 7.

3. What type of distress call should be made in the event of a fire?

    a. 'PAN' call.
    b. 'Help' call.
    c. 'We are declaring an emergency'.
    d. 'MAYDAY'.

4. Should fire drills be memorised?

    a. No.
    b. Yes.
    c. Yes – the 'Memory items' are stipulated in the aircraft checklist.
    d. It depends on what your instructor has taught you.

5. What is the authoritative document on handling emergencies?

   a. Approved Training Organisation's Training Manual.
   b. Approved Training Organisation's Safety Management Manual.
   c. Aircraft Flight Manual/Pilot's Operating Handbook.
   d. AIP.

6. What is the main cause of an engine fire upon start?

   a. Over priming.
   b. Setting the throttle/power lever too far open.
   c. Not setting the mixture control at the rich setting.
   d. A crack in the exhaust pipe.

7. What is the first action after suspecting or detecting a carburettor fire?

   a. Evacuate the aircraft immediately.
   b. Nothing, the engine is designed to cope with the event.
   c. Continue to turn the engine over, and then proceed with the checklist.
   d. Declare a 'MAYDAY' with ATC, and then continue to turn the engine over.

8. Put the following initial generic actions in the correct order for a carburettor fire:

   1. Starter .... Crank engine
   2. Fuel selector .... Off
   3. Throttle .... Open
   4. Fuel selector .... Off
   5. Mixture .... Idle Cut-Off
   6. Electric fuel pump (if fitted) .... Off

9. What are possible indications of a fire or condition that may lead to an engine fire?

   1. Fuel check.
   2. Pressure drop.
   3. Rough running engine.
   4. Flames.
   5. ATC/Ground crew communication.

   a. All of them.
   b. 1,3 & 4.
   c. 1, 2, 3, & 5.
   d. 1 & 5 only.

10. Where will the emergency descent (if any) be described?

    a. In the AFM/POH.

    b. In the checklist.

    c. Light aircraft are not authorised to conduct an emergency descent.

    d. A spiral dive is the safest manoeuvre to descend rapidly.

11. Are the following the correct generic actions for handling an engine fire in flight?

    1. Fuel Selector .... Off

    2. Throttle .... Closed

    3. Mixture....................................... ICO

    4. Electric fuel pump (if fitted) .... Off

    5. Heater....................................... Off

    6. Defroster................................... Off

    7. Execute power-off landing

    a. No, item 7 should be after item 1.

    b. Yes.

    c. No, item 2 should come first.

    d. No, item 4 should come first.

12. For a generic aircraft cabin fire, put the following checklist items in the correct order:

    1. Battery master .... Off

    2. Cabin heat .... Off

    3. Cabin vents .... Open

    a. 1,2,3.

    b. 3,2,1.

    c. 1,3,2.

    d. 2,3,1.

13. How many fire classifications are there?

    a. 3.

    b. 4.

    c. 5.

    d. 6.

3

14.   What is a Class A fire?

    a.   Flammable liquids.
    b.   Metals.
    c.   Electrical.
    d.   Solids.

15.   What is a Class B fire?

    a.   Flammable liquids.
    b.   Metals.
    c.   Electrical.
    d.   Solids.

16.   What is a Class C fire?

    a.   Flammable liquids.
    b.   Metals.
    c.   Electrical.
    d.   Solids.

17.   What is a Class D fire?

    a.   Flammable liquids.
    b.   Metals.
    c.   Electrical.
    d.   Solids.

18.   What is the most common extinguishing agent used in light aircraft?

    a.   Halon.
    b.   Water.
    c.   C02.
    d.   Dry Chemical.

19.   How long does a hand-held fire extinguisher last for?

    a.   60 to 75 seconds.
    b.   30 to 60 seconds.
    c.   8 to 25 seconds.
    d.   120 to 180 seconds.

20.   What are the two main toxic gases within smoke?

    a.   Oxygen and Chloride.
    b.   Oxygen and Hydrogen.
    c.   Carbon Monoxide and Hydrogen Cyanide.
    d.   Carbon Monoxide and BromoChlorodiFluoromethane.

21. What is the purpose of a CO detector?

 a. To detect Carbon Monoxide in the cabin.
 b. To detect Carbon Dioxide in the cabin.
 c. To detect Hydrogen Cyanide in the cabin.
 d. To detect Oxygen in the cabin.

22. Which of the symptoms below may indicate Carbon Monoxide poisoning?

 1. Headache.
 2. Weakness.
 3. Nausea.
 4. Dizziness.
 5. Euphoria.
 6. Enhanced hearing.
 7. Improved vision.

 a. 1,2,6, & 7
 b. All of them.
 c. 1,2,3, & 4.
 d. 3,4,5 & 6.

23. For a generic aircraft suffering from smoke in the cabin, put the following checklist items in the correct order:

 1. Source of fire............................ check

 Electrical fire (smoke in cabin):
 2. Cabin heat .... OFF
 3. Vents....................................... OPEN
 4. Master switch .... OFF

 a. 1,4,3 & 2.
 b. 1,2,3, & 4.
 c. 4,2,3 & 1.
 d. 1,4,2 & 3.

24. What could you do to limit the amount of toxic gases entering your lungs, if you don't have an Oxygen mask?

 a. Put your head out of the door.
 b. Put a sock in your mouth.
 c. Cover your nose and mouth with a damp cloth.
 d. Cover your nose only with a damp cloth.

3

INTENTIONALLY BLANK

3

Questions – Chapter 4

WINDSHEAR AND MICROBURST

1. Any change in the wind speed and/ or the wind direction as you move from one point to another is called a w. . . sh. . .

2. The effect of a windshear that causes an aeroplane to fly above the desired flightpath and/or to increase its speed is called o. . . shoot effect.

3. The effect of a windshear that causes an aeroplane to fly below the desired flightpath and/or to decrease its speed is called u. . . shoot effect.

4. If the initial effect of a windshear is reversed as the aeroplane travels further along its flightpath (say on approach to land), then the overall influence of the windshear on the aeroplane is called a windshear r. . . . effect.

5. Windshear is commonly associated with which of the following types of weather:

   1. Inversions.
   2. Fog.
   3. Rain.
   4. Thunderstorms.
   5. Frontal passage.

   a. 1,2 & 3 only.
   b. All of them.
   c. 1,4 & 5.
   d. 1 & 4 only.

6. During an approach the aircraft is subjected to a windshear with a decreasing headwind component; without pilot intervention the aircraft:

   a. Rate of descent increases, indicated airspeed decreases.
   b. Rate of descent decreases, indicated airspeed decreases.
   c. Rate of descent increases, indicated airspeed increases.
   d. All parameters stay the same.

4

7. During an approach the aircraft is subject to a windshear with an increasing headwind component; without pilot intervention the aircraft:

   a. Rate of descent increases, airspeed decreases.
   b. Rate of descent decreases, airspeed increases.
   c. Rate of descent increases, airspeed increases.
   d. All parameters stay the same.

8. After take-off an aircraft is subject to windshear with an increasing tailwind component; in the absence of pilot intervention:

   a. Nothing happens.
   b. Indicated airspeed reduces, rate of climb decreases.
   c. Indicated airspeed increases, rate of climb decreases.
   d. Indicated airspeed reduces, rate of climb increases.

9. If you see a Thunderstorm overhead the destination airfield, the safest course of action is to:

   a. Hold well clear of the Thunderstorm area, and if necessary divert to a suitable airfield in better weather.
   b. Continue; Thunderstorms are only damaging if an aircraft flies through them.
   c. Let another aircraft attempt an approach first.
   d. Attempt an approach; thunderstorms don't affect light aircraft.

10. You experience windshear on approach to an airfield in the UK, what should you do?

   a. Do not tell anyone.
   b. Inform ATC once safely on the ground and submit a MOR to the UK CAA.
   c. Inform your instructor only.
   d. Inform your family upon return.

11. Indications of a Microburst may be provided by:

   1. Thunderstorms.
   2. Pilot reports.
   3. ATS warning.
   4. Initial increase in airspeed and reduced rate of descent at a constant pitch and power setting.
   5. Initial decrease in airspeed and reduced rate of descent at a constant pitch and power setting.

   a. 1 and 5 only.
   b. All of them.
   c. 1,2,3 & 4.
   d. 1,2,3 & 5.

Questions – Chapter 5

WAKE TURBULENCE

1. The static air pressure beneath a wing is (greater than/less than) the static air pressure above the wing.

2. The air beneath a wing of an aeroplane in flight tends to leak around the wingtip and into the lower static pressure area above the wing. This leaves a trail of invisible w. . . . . v . . . .s behind.

3. These wingtip vortices can be very strong behind a heavy aeroplane flying slowly at a high a. . . . . of a. . . . ., such as on take-off and landing.

4. Wingtip vortices tend to drift (up/down).

5. Wingtip vortices tend to (drift downwind/drift upwind/remain stationary over the ground, even in steady winds).

6. You should (disregard/avoid) wake turbulence behind a heavy jet that has just taken-off.

7. The most dangerous area for wake turbulence behind a heavy jet is (at the start of his take-off run/just past his point of rotation and on his climb-out).

8. Wake turbulence (is different from/the same as) 'jet blast'.

9. Which scenario from the answers below, is likely to create the largest amount of wake turbulence:
   a. Large aeroplane, flying slowly, flaps retracted in light winds.
   b. Small aeroplane, flying slowly, flaps retracted in light winds.
   c. Large aeroplane, flying fast, flaps retracted.
   d. Small aeroplane, flying fast, flaps retracted.

10. Wake turbulence is created once an aircraft creates lift, and/or a helicopter enters a hover?

    a. True, or False?

11. A light aircraft following an Airbus A380 requires a minimum separation of how many nautical miles?

    a. 4 NM
    b. 5 NM
    c. 7 NM
    d. 8 NM

12. Wake turbulence:

    a. Only occurs when an aircraft is in the cruise phase of flight.
    b. Is confined to helicopters.
    c. Is produced by all lighter than air vessels.
    d. Is produced when an aircraft generates lift or when a helicopter hovers.

13. Wake turbulence:

    a. Is produced by an aircraft's jet engine.
    b. Is a hazard to a light aircraft taxiing within 3 rotor dimensions of a hovering helicopter.
    c. Is produced by an aircraft when it is on the ground.
    d. Is an aircraft only phenomenon.

14. In which of the following scenarios could a wake turbulence encounter occur?

    a. Departing from a crossing runway after another aircraft rotated beyond the intersection.
    b. Upwind of an aircraft that has executed a missed approach.
    c. Crossing behind a 'Heavy' aircraft 1000ft above, on an approach.
    d. Landing on a crossing runway after another aircraft rotated prior to the intersection.

Questions – Chapter 6

EMERGENCY & PRECAUTIONARY LANDINGS

1. What is the definition of distress?

   a. A condition of being threatened by serious and/or imminent danger and of requiring immediate assistance.

   b. A condition concerning the safety of an aircraft or other vehicle, or of some person on board or within sight, but which does not require immediate assistance.

   c. Any time the Pilot-in-Command is apprehensive.

   d. A condition of being stressed by serious and/or imminent danger and of requiring immediate assistance.

2. What is the definition of urgency?

   a. A condition concerning the safety of an aircraft or other vehicle.

   b. A condition concerning the safety of an aircraft or other vehicle, or of some person on board or within sight, but which does not require immediate assistance.

   c. A condition where the Pilot-in-Command wants to a get home quickly.

   d. A condition of being threatened by serious and/or imminent danger and of requiring immediate assistance.

3. From the answers below which are the international distress frequencies?

   1. 121.500 MHz
   2. 123.450 MHz
   3. 243.00 MHz
   4. 1215 MHz

   a. 2 & 3.
   b. 1 & 3.
   c. 1,2 & 4.
   d. 1 & 4.

4. If an engine fails in flight in a single engine aircraft that is over land, what are the correct generic actions?

    a. Trim for the best glide speed, plan a forced landing pattern, declare a 'MAYDAY', check fuel selector ON and change fuel tanks, mixture rich, carburettor heat on, check engine gauges, primer locked, magnetos on both – attempt restart.

    b. Declare a MAYDAY and if you have a parachute abandon the aircraft immediately.

    c. Trim for the best glide speed, plan a forced landing pattern, declare a 'MAYDAY', throttle closed, mixture ICO, fuel selector off, magnetos off, battery master off.

    d. Do nothing; the engine will come back to life in its own time.

5. What is the emergency transponder code?

    a. 7500.

    b. 7600.

    c. 7700.

    d. 7000.

6. Regarding life jackets:

    a. The Pilot-in-Command should inflate his life jacket before exiting the aircraft and instruct the passengers to do the same.

    b. The passengers should inflate their jackets before ditching, however the Pilot-in-Command should wait until after exiting the aircraft.

    c. Both the Pilot-in-Command and passengers should inflate their life jackets once outside the aircraft.

    d. It doesn't matter.

7. When ditching the pilot should:

    a. Land as slowly as possible into a rising swell, with a strong headwind.

    b. Land as slowly as possible, declare a 'MAYDAY', and squawk 7700 as early as possible.

    c. Glide at best range speed to allow the longest time airborne.

    d. Glide at best range speed, squawk 7600, and turn away from any shipping.

8. In a ditching scenario, the pilot should instruct passengers to don life jackets and inflate them:

    a. In the aircraft.

    b. Once in the dinghy, or if no dinghy is available once in the water.

    c. Outside the aircraft but before entering the water, or dinghy if one is available.

    d. Once in the water.

9.   In a ditching situation best practice is to:

   a.   Inflate a life jacket before ditching to give crash protection.
   b.   Inflate a life jacket using the manual inflation tube once in the water.
   c.   Inflate a life jacket before completing a running jump off the fuselage.
   d.   Inflate a life jacket after leaving the aircraft but before entering the dinghy or the water if no dinghy is available.

10.   In the event of a planned emergency on land instruct passengers:

   a.   To remove all sharp objects, dentures and high-heeled shoes – stow in passenger compartments or under the seat.
   b.   Not to panic.
   c.   Turn on all mobile phones.
   d.   Loosen seat belts ready for evacuation.

11.   When should the command 'BRACE BRACE' be given?

   a.   15 minutes before impact.
   b.   15 seconds before impact.
   c.   25 seconds before impact.
   d.   5 seconds before impact.

12.   In the event of an evacuation what are the generic actions to shut down the aircraft and limit the risk of a fire?

   a.   Battery master off, fuel on, ignition 'OFF', run.
   b.   Throttle closed, master switch 'OFF', fuel selector 'OFF', mixture ICO.
   c.   Throttle closed, master switch 'ON', fuel selector 'ON', mixture ICO.
   d.   Getting out of the aircraft is the most important action, you can always return.

13.   Which of the actions listed below should be carried out after an evacuation on land?

   1.   Direct passengers upwind of the aircraft.
   2.   Go to the nearest public house.
   3.   Administer first aid as required.
   4.   Conduct a head count.
   5.   Contact the emergency services.
   6.   Activate Personal Locator Beacons if in a remote location.
   7.   Drain all fuel, to reduce the risk of fire.
   8.   Attempt an engine restart and if successful, fly the aircraft out of the landing site back to base.

   a.   All of them.
   b.   2 & 5.
   c.   All except 2, 7 & 8.
   d.   1,2 & 7.

6

INTENTIONALLY BLANK

Questions – Chapter 7

CONTAMINATED RUNWAYS

1. What is the definition of a 'WET' runway?

    a. The surface is soaked but no significant patches of standing water are visible.
    b. Significant patches of standing water are visible.
    c. It is damp to touch.
    d. Extensive patches of standing water are visible.

2. Which of the following statements is correct regarding operations on a contaminated runway?

    a. Operations by all aircraft classes and types should be avoided whenever possible.
    b. Whenever a departure from a contaminated runway is unavoidable, adopt the short field take-off technique.
    c. Whenever a departure from a contaminated runway is unavoidable, use the full length of the runway available, the lowest take-off flap setting possible and maximum take-off power.
    d. Operations from contaminated runways require little risk assessment by the Pilot-in-Command.

3. A runway is classed as contaminated if it is:

    a. 'DRY'.
    b. Notified as 'WET'.
    c. Notified as having 'WATER PATCHES'.
    d. Notified as 'DAMP'.

4. ATC report to you that the runway is 'FLOODED', this means that:

    a. Extensive patches of standing water are visible.
    b. The runway is safe to use.
    c. Significant patches of standing water are visible.
    d. This term only applies to large aeroplanes.

5. With regard to contaminated runway operations which of the following statements is true?

    a. The friction coefficient increases with the amount of precipitation on the runway.
    b. The friction coefficient on ice increases therefore the landing distance reduces.
    c. Both departure and arrival on a contaminated runway by any aircraft should be avoided if possible.
    d. A pilot should use a reduced power setting for take-off on a contaminated runway.

6. ATC report to you that the runway is 'WET', is the runway contaminated?

    a. No.
    b. Yes.
    c. This term only applies to large aircraft.
    d. Only if more than 20% is covered with a depth greater than 2 mm.

7. A runway is said to be contaminated if it:

    a. Is 'WET'.
    b. Has greater than 3 mm of slush over 22% of the surface area.
    c. Has ice covering more than 25% of the runway surface area within the required width and length.
    d. Is 'DAMP'.

Answers – Chapter 1

OPERATION OF AIRCRAFT

1. What is definition of a large aeroplane?

    a. An aeroplane of a maximum certificated take-off mass of over 5700 kg.
    b. A jet aeroplane with more than 9 seats.
    c. Any aeroplane with more than 9 seats.
    d. Any aircraft with more than 1 engine.

2. What is the definition of the pilot-in-command?

    a. The pilot who has the most flying experience on board the aircraft
    b. The pilot who sits in the left hand seat.
    c. The pilot designated by the operator or the owner as being in command and charged with the safe conduct of a flight.
    d. The pilot designated by the operator, or the owner as being the person who makes all the critical decisions in flight.

3. What is definition of night?

    a. Anytime that Air Traffic Control put the runway lights on.
    b. The hours between the end of evening civil twilight and the beginning of morning civil twilight, or such other period between sunset and sunrise, as may be prescribed by the appropriate authority.
    c. The hours between evening civil twilight and the morning civil twilight or such other period between sunset and sunrise, as may be prescribed by the appropriate authority.
    d. Anytime the pilot-in-command cannot see sunlight.

4. What is definition of the Operator?

    a. The person charged by the CAA to operate the aircraft.
    b. The pilot-in-command.
    c. The person or organisation that pays the bills.
    d. A person, organisation, or enterprise engaged in, or offering to engage in an aircraft operation.

5.   What is the definition of Flight Time — aeroplanes?

    a.   The total time from the moment an aeroplane first moves for the purpose of taking off until the moment it finally comes to rest at the end of the flight.

    b.   The total time from the moment an aeroplane first gets airborne until the moment it finally touches down.

    c.   The moment you 'book out' with operations to moment you 'book in'.

    d.   The total time the engine is running.

6.   What is the ICAO definition of Aerial Work?

    a.   Any aircraft operation in which an aircraft is being funded from a commercial venture.

    b.   An aircraft operation in which an aircraft is used for specialised services such as agriculture, construction, photography, surveying, observation and patrol, search and rescue, aerial advertisement, etc.

    c.   Any aircraft operation in which the pilot-in-command is required to hold a Commercial Pilot's Licence.

    d.   An aircraft operation in which an aircraft is used for specialised services such as agriculture, construction, photography, surveying, observation and patrol, search and rescue, private hire and scheduled travel, etc.

7.   What is a Flight Manual?

    a.   A manual which describes the national aviation authorities' Rules of the Air and associated ICAO differences.

    b.   A manual or book which describes how to operate the aircraft.

    c.   A manual, associated with the certificate of airworthiness, containing limitations within which the aircraft is to be considered airworthy, and instructions and information necessary to the flight crew members for the safe operation of the aircraft.

    d.   A manual containing limitations within which the aircraft is to be considered airworthy, and instructions and information necessary to the flight crew members for the safe operation of the aircraft.

8.   What is the definition of a General Aviation Operation?

    a.   An aircraft operation other than a commercial air transport operation or an aerial work operation.

    b.   An aircraft operation that is general in nature.

    c.   An aircraft operation other than a commercial air transport operation or an aerial work operation that uses light aircraft.

    d.   An aircraft operation other than a commercial air transport operation or an aerial work operation that uses single engine piston aircraft.

9. What is an Operations Manual?

   a. A manual containing procedures, instructions and guidance for use by operational personnel in the execution of their duties.

   b. A manual or book containing procedures, instructions, and guidance for use by operational personnel in the execution of their duties.

   c. A manual containing procedures, instructions and guidance for use by Operations personnel only.

   d. A manual, associated with the certificate of airworthiness, containing limitations within which the aircraft is to be considered airworthy, and instructions and information necessary to the flight crew members for the safe operation of the aircraft.

10. What is the State of Registry?

   a. The State whose monarchy owns the aircraft.

   b. The State on whose register the aircraft is entered.

   c. The country where the insurance company is registered.

   d. The state where the aircraft is based.

11. What is a Safety Management System?

   a. A systematic approach to managing safety, including the necessary organisational structures, accountabilities, policies, and procedures.

   b. A systematic approach to managing the owners of flying schools, including the necessary organisational structures, accountabilities, policies, and procedures.

   c. A system devised by the Health and Safety Executive to monitor managers of flying schools and other aviation businesses.

   d. A manual containing procedures, instructions and guidance for use by operational personnel in the execution of their duties.

1

INTENTIONALLY BLANK

1

Answers – Chapter 2

NOISE ABATEMENT

1. Can the CAA prosecute a pilot for breaking an airfield's Noise Abatement Procedures?

    a. Yes, the CAA can prosecute a pilot for anything they wish.

    b. No, the CAA can only prosecute a pilot for breaking the ANO and Rules of the Air.

    c. It depends on the size and location of the airfield.

    d. The CAA will prosecute a pilot when asked to do so by an airfield operator.

2. Where would you find Noise Abatement Procedures for a licensed airfield?

    a. In the applicable airfield entry in the AIP.

    b. In the ANO.

    c. Each airfield's Noise Abatement Procedures are published in an AIC.

    d. You MUST ring the ATSU for a verbal briefing.

3. Where would you find Noise Abatement Procedures for an unlicensed airfield?

    a. In the applicable airfield entry in the AIP.

    b. In the ANO.

    c. Each airfield's Noise Abatement Procedures are published in an AIC.

    d. In a commercial flight guide such as 'Pooley's Flight Guide'.

4. Should you cross Stop Bars at a runway holding point?

    a. Yes, these are only for large aeroplanes.

    b. Yes, they might be faulty.

    c. No, wait until they have been extinguished by ATC.

    d. Only if you see them.

5. Before entering a runway what should you do regarding lookout?

    a. Look both left and right to check the approach and runway are clear.

    b. Turn off all aircraft lights in order not to dazzle other pilots.

    c. Do nothing; it is ATC responsibility to check that the runway is clear.

    d. Taxi onto the runway very slowly, stop and apply the parking brake, complete the before take-off checklist.

6.   Do Noise Abatement Procedures apply to PPL holders?

   a.   No, only to Commercial Pilots
   b.   No, PPL holders generally do not operate at larger airfields, which are the only types
            that have Noise Abatement Procedures.
   c.   No, PPL holders are immune from any penalty that the airfield operator may impose
            on them for disregarding their Noise Abatement Procedures.
   d.   Yes, as most airfields now have Noise Abatement Procedures, PPL holders should
            follow them.

7.   The position of runway holding points ensures:

   a.   That a safe gap exists between the aircraft holding and any aircraft that may pass in
            front of it.
   b.   That a safe gap exists between the aircraft holding and any aircraft that may pass in
            front of, or behind it.
   c.   Nothing is assured-it is the pilot-in-command's responsibility.
   d.   That a safe gap exists to protect the radio signals for the applicable instrument
            approach only.

8.   When lining up on a runway the pilot should:

   1.   Look left and right to check for aircraft or vehicles on the runway.
   2.   Ensure a clearance has been given.
   3.   Put all aircraft lights and transponder on.
   4.   Taxi very slowly onto the runway and always stop and apply the parking brake.

   a.   1,2 & 4.
   b.   All of them.
   c.   1,2 & 3.
   d.   1 & 4.

9.   If in doubt about the correct route to follow whilst taxiing the pilot should:

   a.   Bring the aircraft to a stop, inform ATC, and ask for clarification.
   b.   Bring the aircraft to a stop, shutdown the engine and call ATC using a mobile phone.
   c.   Bring the aircraft to a stop, inform ATC, and call the flying school.
   d.   Keep moving at all times; ATC need to ensure that an efficient flow of traffic exists at
            all times.

10. What is the correct phraseology for the issue of a take-off clearance?

   a.   ATC: G-CD, cleared for take-off. Pilot: Cleared for take-off, G-CD.
   b.   ATC: G-CD, cleared for departure. Pilot: Cleared for departure, G-CD.
   c.   ATC: G-CD, cleared to go. Pilot: Cleared to go, G-CD.
   d.   ATC: G-CD, cleared to light the fires. Pilot: Cleared to light the fires, G-CD.

2

11. Should a clearance limit be written down?

    a. Yes.

    b. No.

    c. Depends on the pilot's mental capacity.

    d. Only if the pilot is not familiar with the airport.

12. What is the colour of runway Stop Bars and Guard Lights respectively?

    a. Red and Yellow.

    b. Yellow and Blue.

    c. Blue and Green.

    d. Red and White.

13. Regarding taxiing procedures at airports with ATC which of the following statements is correct?

    1. The position of the runway holding point ensures that a sufficient margin exists between the holding aircraft, and any aircraft passing in front of it.

    2. You may cross a runway Stop Bar, once a clearance has been received by ATC and they have been extinguished.

    3. You may cross two solid and two broken yellow lines only after a specific clearance to do so has been given and after you have checked both left and right for traffic.

    4. You may cross a dashed yellow line only after a specific clearance to do so has been given.

    a. 1, 2, & 3.

    b. All of them.

    c. 1 & 4 only.

    d. 1, 2, & 4.

2

INTENTIONALLY BLANK

2

Answers – Chapter 3

FIRE OR SMOKE

1. How many components must a fire have?

    a. 2.
    b. 3.
    c. 4.
    d. 5.

2. What are the four major phases/causes of aircraft fire?

    1. Engine start.
    2. Circuits.
    3. Electrical.
    4. Re-fuelling.
    5. Post-crash.
    6. Inflight.
    7. Passengers smoking.

    a. All of them.
    b. 1, 2, 5, & 6.
    c. 1, 3, 5, & 6.
    d. 2, 3, 5, & 7.

3. What type of distress call should be made in the event of a fire?

    a. 'PAN' call.
    b. 'Help' call.
    c. 'We are declaring an emergency'.
    d. 'MAYDAY'.

4. Should fire drills be memorised?

    a. No.
    b. Yes.
    c. Yes – the 'Memory items' are stipulated in the aircraft checklist.
    d. It depends on what your instructor has taught you.

5.   What is the authoritative document on handling emergencies?

   a.   Approved Training Organisation's Training Manual.
   b.   Approved Training Organisation's Safety Management Manual.
   c.   Aircraft Flight Manual/Pilot's Operating Handbook.
   d.   AIP.

6.   What is the main cause of an engine fire upon start?

   a.   Over priming.
   b.   Setting the throttle/power lever too far open.
   c.   Not setting the mixture control at the rich setting.
   d.   A crack in the exhaust pipe.

7.   What is the first action after suspecting or detecting a carburettor fire?

   a.   Evacuate the aircraft immediately.
   b.   Nothing, the engine is designed to cope with the event.
   c.   Continue to turn the engine over, and then proceed with the checklist.
   d.   Declare a 'MAYDAY' with ATC, and then continue to turn the engine over.

8.   Put the following initial generic actions in the correct order
         for a carburettor fire: Answer 1,5,3,6 & 2

   1.   Starter .... Crank engine
   2.   Fuel selector .... Off
   3.   Throttle .... Open
   4.   Fuel selector .... Off
   5.   Mixture .... Idle Cut-Off
   6.   Electric fuel pump (if fitted) .... Off

9.   What are possible indications of a fire or condition that may lead to an
         engine fire?

   1.   Fuel check.
   2.   Pressure drop.
   3.   Rough running engine.
   4.   Flames.
   5.   ATC/Ground crew communication.

   a.   All of them.
   b.   1,3 & 4.
   c.   1, 2, 3, & 5.
   d.   1 & 5 only.

3

FIRE OR SMOKE – ANSWERS

10. Where will the emergency descent (if any) be described?

    a. In the AFM/POH.
    b. In the checklist.
    c. Light aircraft are not authorised to conduct an emergency descent.
    d. A spiral dive is the safest manoeuvre to descend rapidly.

11. Are the following the correct generic actions for handling an engine fire in flight?

    1. Fuel Selector................................ Off
    2. Throttle .... Closed
    3. Mixture....................................... ICO
    4. Electric fuel pump (if fitted).............. Off
    5. Heater....................................... Off
    6. Defroster.................................... Off
    7. Execute power-off landing

    a. No, item 7 should be after item 1.
    b. Yes.
    c. No, item 2 should come first.
    d. No, item 4 should come first.

12. For a generic aircraft cabin fire, put the following checklist items in the correct order:

    1. Battery master .... Off
    2. Cabin heat .... Off
    3. Cabin vents................................. Open

    a. 1,2,3.
    b. 3,2,1.
    c. 1,3,2.
    d. 2,3,1.

13. How many fire classifications are there?

    a. 3.
    b. 4.
    c. 5.
    d. 6.

3

14.   What is a Class A fire?

    a.   Flammable liquids.
    b.   Metals.
    c.   Electrical.
    d.   **Solids.**

15.   What is a Class B fire?

    a.   **Flammable liquids.**
    b.   Metals.
    c.   Electrical.
    d.   Solids.

16.   What is a Class C fire?

    a.   Flammable liquids.
    b.   Metals.
    c.   **Electrical.**
    d.   Solids.

17.   What is a Class D fire?

    a.   Flammable liquids.
    b.   **Metals.**
    c.   Electrical.
    d.   Solids.

18.   What is the most common extinguishing agent used in light aircraft?

    a.   Halon.
    b.   Water.
    c.   CO2.
    d.   Dry Chemical.

19.   How long does a hand-held fire extinguisher last for?

    a.   60 to 75 seconds.
    b.   30 to 60 seconds.
    c.   **8 to 25 seconds.**
    d.   120 to 180 seconds.

20.   What are the two main toxic gases within smoke?

    a.   Oxygen and Chloride.
    b.   Oxygen and Hydrogen.
    c.   **Carbon Monoxide and Hydrogen Cyanide.**
    d.   Carbon Monoxide and BromoChlorodiFluoromethane.

21. What is the purpose of a CO detector?

   a. To detect Carbon Monoxide in the cabin.
   b. To detect Carbon Dioxide in the cabin.
   c. To detect Hydrogen Cyanide in the cabin.
   d. To detect Oxygen in the cabin.

22. Which of the symptoms below may indicate Carbon Monoxide poisoning?

   1. Headache.
   2. Weakness.
   3. Nausea.
   4. Dizziness.
   5. Euphoria.
   6. Enhanced hearing.
   7. Improved vision.

   a. 1,2,6, & 7
   b. All of them.
   c. 1,2,3, & 4.
   d. 3,4,5 & 6.

23. For a generic aircraft suffering from smoke in the cabin, put the following checklist items in the correct order:

   1. Source of fire.............................. check

   Electrical fire (smoke in cabin):
   2. Cabin heat .... OFF
   3. Vents.. OPEN
   4. Master switch .... OFF

   a. 1,4,3 & 2.
   b. 1,2,3, & 4.
   c. 4,2,3 & 1.
   d. 1,4,2 & 3.

24. What could you do to limit the amount of toxic gases entering your lungs, if you don't have an Oxygen mask?

   a. Put your head out of the door.
   b. Put a sock in your mouth.
   c. Cover your nose and mouth with a damp cloth.
   d. Cover your nose only with a damp cloth.

INTENTIONALLY BLANK

3

Answers – Chapter 4

WINDSHEAR AND MICROBURST

1.   Any change in the wind speed and/ or the wind direction as you move from one point to another is called a windshear.

2.   The effect of a windshear that causes an aeroplane to fly above the desired flightpath and/or to increase its speed is called overshoot effect.

3.   The effect of a windshear that causes an aeroplane to fly below the desired flightpath and/or to decrease its speed is called undershoot effect.

4.   If the initial effect of a windshear is reversed as the aeroplane travels further along its flightpath (say on approach to land), then the overall influence of the windshear on the aeroplane is called a windshear reversal effect.

5.   Windshear is commonly associated with which of the following types of weather:

   1.   Inversions.
   2.   Fog.
   3.   Rain.
   4.   Thunderstorms.
   5.   Frontal passage.

   a.   1,2 & 3 only.
   b.   All of them.
   c.   1,4 & 5.
   d.   1 & 4 only.

6.   During an approach the aircraft is subjected to a windshear with a decreasing headwind component; without pilot intervention the aircraft:

   a.   Rate of descent increases, indicated airspeed decreases.
   b.   Rate of descent decreases, indicated airspeed decreases.
   c.   Rate of descent increases, indicated airspeed increases.
   d.   All parameters stay the same.

4

7. During an approach the aircraft is subject to a windshear with an increasing headwind component; without pilot intervention the aircraft:

a. Rate of descent increases, airspeed decreases.
b. Rate of descent decreases, airspeed increases.
c. Rate of descent increases, airspeed increases.
d. All parameters stay the same.

8. After take-off an aircraft is subject to windshear with an increasing tailwind component; in the absence of pilot intervention:

a. Nothing happens.
b. Indicated airspeed reduces, rate of climb decreases.
c. Indicated airspeed increases, rate of climb decreases.
d. Indicated airspeed reduces, rate of climb increases.

9. If you see a Thunderstorm overhead the destination airfield, the safest course of action is to:

a. Hold well clear of the Thunderstorm area, and if necessary divert to a suitable airfield in better weather.
b. Continue; Thunderstorms are only damaging if an aircraft flies through them.
c. Let another aircraft attempt an approach first.
d. Attempt an approach; thunderstorms don't affect light aircraft.

10. You experience windshear on approach to an airfield in the UK, what should you do?

a. Do not tell anyone.
b. Inform ATC once safely on the ground and submit a MOR to the UK CAA.
c. Inform your instructor only.
d. Inform your family upon return.

11. Indications of a Microburst may be provided by:

1. Thunderstorms.
2. Pilot reports.
3. ATS warning.
4. Initial increase in airspeed and reduced rate of descent at a constant pitch and power setting.
5. Initial decrease in airspeed and reduced rate of descent at a constant pitch and power setting.

a. 1 and 5 only.
b. All of them.
c. 1,2,3 & 4.
d. 1,2,3 & 5.

4

Answers – Chapter 5

WAKE TURBULENCE

1. The static air pressure beneath a wing is (greater than/less than) the static air pressure above the wing.

2. The air beneath a wing of an aeroplane in flight tends to leak around the wingtip and into the lower static pressure area above the wing. This leaves a trail of invisible wingtip vortices behind.

3. These wingtip vortices can be very strong behind a heavy aeroplane flying slowly at a high angle of attack, such as on take-off and landing.

4. Wingtip vortices tend to drift (up/down).

5. Wingtip vortices tend to (drift downwind/drift upwind/remain stationary over the ground, even in steady winds).

6. You should (disregard/avoid) wake turbulence behind a heavy jet that has just taken-off.

7. The most dangerous area for wake turbulence behind a heavy jet is (at the start of his take-off run/just past his point of rotation and on his climb-out).

8. Wake turbulence (is different from/the same as) 'jet blast'.

9. Which scenario from the answers below, is likely to create the largest amount of wake turbulence:

a. Large aeroplane, flying slowly, flaps retracted in light winds.
b. Small aeroplane, flying slowly, flaps retracted in light winds.
c. Large aeroplane, flying fast, flaps retracted.
d. Small aeroplane, flying fast, flaps retracted.

10. Wake turbulence is created once an aircraft creates lift, and/or a helicopter enters a hover?

    a. True, or False?

11. A light aircraft following an Airbus A380 requires a minimum separation of how many nautical miles?

    a. 4 NM
    b. 5 NM
    c. 7 NM
    d. 8 NM

12. Wake turbulence:

    a. Only occurs when an aircraft is in the cruise phase of flight.
    b. Is confined to helicopters.
    c. Is produced by all lighter than air vessels.
    d. Is produced when an aircraft generates lift or when a helicopter hovers.

13. Wake turbulence:

    a. Is produced by an aircraft's jet engine.
    b. Is a hazard to a light aircraft taxiing within 3 rotor dimensions of a hovering helicopter.
    c. Is produced by an aircraft when it is on the ground.
    d. Is an aircraft only phenomenon.

14. In which of the following scenarios could a wake turbulence encounter occur?

    a. Departing from a crossing runway after another aircraft rotated beyond the intersection.
    b. Upwind of an aircraft that has executed a missed approach.
    c. Crossing behind a 'Heavy' aircraft 1000ft above, on an approach.
    d. Landing on a crossing runway after another aircraft rotated prior to the intersection.

Answers – Chapter 6

EMERGENCY & PRECAUTIONARY LANDINGS

1. What is the definition of distress?

    a. A condition of being threatened by serious and/or imminent danger and of requiring immediate assistance.

    b. A condition concerning the safety of an aircraft or other vehicle, or of some person on board or within sight, but which does not require immediate assistance.

    c. Any time the pilot-in-command is apprehensive.

    d. A condition of being stressed by serious and/or imminent danger and of requiring immediate assistance.

2. What is the definition of urgency?

    a. A condition concerning the safety of an aircraft or other vehicle.

    b. A condition concerning the safety of an aircraft or other vehicle, or of some person on board or within sight, but which does not require immediate assistance.

    c. A condition where the pilot-in-command wants to get home quickly.

    d. A condition of being threatened by serious and/or imminent danger and of requiring immediate assistance.

3. From the answers below which are the international distress frequencies?

    1. 121.500 MHz
    2. 123.450 MHz
    3. 243.00 MHz
    4. 1215 MHz

    a. 2 & 3.
    b. 1 & 3.
    c. 1,2 & 4.
    d. 1 & 4.

4. If an engine fails in flight in a single engine aircraft that is over land, what are the correct generic actions?

a. Trim for the best glide speed, plan a forced landing pattern, declare a 'MAYDAY', check fuel selector ON and change fuel tanks, mixture rich, carburettor heat on, check engine gauges, primer locked, magnetos on both – attempt restart.

b. Declare a MAYDAY and if you have a parachute abandon the aircraft immediately.

c. Trim for the best glide speed, plan a forced landing pattern, declare a 'MAYDAY', throttle closed, mixture ICO, fuel selector off, magnetos off, battery master off.

d. Do nothing; the engine will come back to life in its own time.

5. What is the emergency transponder code?

a. 7500.
b. 7600.
c. 7700.
d. 7000.

6. Regarding life jackets:

a. The pilot-in-command should inflate his life jacket before exiting the aircraft and instruct the passengers to do the same.

b. The passengers should inflate their jackets before ditching, however the pilot-in-command should wait until after exiting the aircraft.

c. Both the pilot-in-command and passengers should inflate their life jackets once outside the aircraft.

d. It doesn't matter.

7. When ditching the pilot should:

a. Land as slowly as possible into a rising swell, with a strong headwind.
b. Land as slowly as possible, declare a 'MAYDAY', and squawk 7700 as early as possible.
c. Glide at best range speed to allow the longest time airborne.
d. Glide at best range speed, squawk 7600, and turn away from any shipping.

8. In a ditching scenario, the pilot should instruct passengers to don life jackets and inflate them:

a. In the aircraft.
b. Once in the dinghy, or if no dinghy is available once in the water.
c. Outside of the aircraft but before entering the water, or dinghy if one is available.
d. Once in the water.

9.   In a ditching situation best practice is to:

    a.   Inflate a life jacket before ditching to give crash protection.

    b.   Inflate a life jacket using the manual inflation tube once in the water.

    c.   Inflate a life jacket before completing a running jump off the fuselage.

    d.   Inflate a life jacket after leaving the aircraft but before entering the dinghy or the water if no dinghy is available.

10.   In the event of a planned emergency on land instruct passengers:

    a.   To remove all sharp objects, dentures and high-heeled shoes – stow in passenger compartments or under the seat.

    b.   Not to panic.

    c.   Turn on all mobile phones.

    d.   Loosen seat belts ready for evacuation.

11.   When should the command 'BRACE BRACE' be given?

    a.   15 minutes before impact.

    b.   15 seconds before impact.

    c.   25 seconds before impact.

    d.   5 seconds before impact.

12.   In the event of an evacuation what are the generic actions to shut down the aircraft and limit the risk of a fire?

    a.   Battery master off, fuel on, ignition 'OFF', run.

    b.   Throttle closed, master switch 'OFF', fuel selector 'OFF', mixture ICO.

    c.   Throttle closed, master switch 'ON', fuel selector 'ON', mixture ICO.

    d.   Getting out of the aircraft is the most important action, you can always return.

13.   Which of the actions listed below should be carried out after an evacuation on land?

    1.   Direct passengers upwind of the aircraft.

    2.   Go to the nearest public house.

    3.   Administer first aid as required.

    4.   Conduct a head count.

    5.   Contact the emergency services.

    6.   Activate Personal Locator Beacons if in a remote location.

    7.   Drain all fuel, to reduce the risk of fire.

    8.   Attempt an engine restart and if successful, fly the aircraft out of the landing site back to base.

    a.   All of them.

    b.   2 & 5.

    c.   All except 2, 7 & 8.

    d.   1, 2 & 7.

6

INTENTIONALLY BLANK

Answers – Chapter 7

CONTAMINATED RUNWAYS

1. What is the definition of a 'WET' runway?

    a. The surface is soaked but no significant patches of standing water are visible.
    b. Significant patches of standing water are visible.
    c. It is damp to touch.
    d. Extensive patches of standing water are visible.

2. Which of the following statements is correct regarding operations on a contaminated runway?

    a. Operations by all aircraft classes and types should be avoided whenever possible.
    b. Whenever a departure from a contaminated runway is unavoidable, adopt the short field take-off technique.
    c. Whenever a departure from a contaminated runway is unavoidable, use the full length of the runway available, the lowest take-off flap setting possible and maximum take-off power.
    d. Operations from contaminated runways require little risk assessment by the Pilot-in-Command.

3. A runway is classed as contaminated if it is:

    a. 'DRY'.
    b. Notified as 'WET'.
    c. Notified as having 'WATER PATCHES'.
    d. Notified as 'DAMP'.

4. ATC report to you that the runway is 'FLOODED', this means that:

    a. Extensive patches of standing water are visible.
    b. The runway is safe to use.
    c. Significant patches of standing water are visible.
    d. This term only applies to large aeroplanes.

5. With regard to contaminated runway operations which of the following statements is true?

    a. The friction coefficient increases with the amount of precipitation on the runway.
    b. The friction coefficient on ice increases therefore the landing distance reduces.
    c. Both departure and arrival on a contaminated runway by any aircraft should be avoided if possible.
    d. A pilot should use a reduced power setting for take-off on a contaminated runway.

6. ATC report to you that the runway is 'WET', is the runway contaminated?

 a. No.
 b. Yes.
 c. This term only applies to large aircraft.
 d. Only if more than 20% is covered with a depth greater than 2 mm.

7. A runway is said to be contaminated if it:

 a. Is 'WET'.
 b. Has greater than 3 mm of slush over 22% of the surface area.
 c. Has ice covering more than 25% of the runway surface area within the required width and length.
 d. Is 'DAMP'.

Abbreviations

A/G	Air to Ground
A320	Airbus A320
AFM	Aircraft Flight Manual
AIC	Aeronautical Information Circular
AIP	Aeronautical Information Publication
ANSV	Agenzia Nazionale per la Sicurezza del Volo
AOM	Aerodrome Operating Minima
APM	Air Pilot Manual
ASDA	Accelerate Stop Distance Available
ATC	Air Traffic Control
ATSU	Air Traffic Service Unit
AVGAS	Aviation Gasoline
BCF	BromoChlorodiFluoromethane
CAA	Civil Aviation Authority
CAT	Category
CFME	Continuous Friction Measuring Equipment
CFMU	Continuous Friction Measuring Unit
CO$_2$	Carbon Dioxide
DA	Decision Altitude
EASA	European Aviation Safety Agency
ECU	Engine Control Unit
ELT	Emergency Locator Transmitter
EU-OPS	European Operations
EVS	Enhanced Vision System
FCL	Flight Crew Licensing
FISO	Flight Information Service Officer
FSTD	Flight Synthetic Training Device
HALON	Halogenated hydrocarbons
HUD	Head Up Display

ICAO	International Civil Aviation Organisation
ICO	Idle Cut Off
ILS	Instrument Landing System
IMC	Instrument Metrological Conditions
LAPL	Light Aircraft Pilots Licence
LVPs	Low Visibility Procedures
MDA	Minimum Descent Altitude
MTOW	Maximum Take-Off Weight
NAP	Noise Abatement Procedure
NOTAM	Notice To Airmen
NPR	Noise Preferential Routing
PIC	Pilot-in-Command
PIREPS	Pilot Reports
POH	Pilot's Operating Handbook
PPL	Private Pilots Licence
RCC	Rescue Coordination Centre
RNAV	Area Navigation
RVR	Runway Visual Range
SA	Situation Awareness
SNOWTAM	Snow Notice To Airmen
TCDSN	Type-Certificate Data Sheet for Noise
VFE	Velocity Flap Extension
VLE	Velocity Leg Extension
VMC	Visual Meteorological Conditions
VNO	Velocity Normal Operation

Index